The autistic spectrum – a handbook 1999

THE NATIONAL
AUTISTIC SOCIETY

ISBN 1-899280-02-2

9 781899 280025

The National Autistic Society

Patron – HRH The Princess Royal

President – Jane Asher

Chairman – Judy Lusty

Chief Executive – Paul Cann

Mission Statement

The National Autistic Society exists to champion the rights and interests of all people with autism and to ensure that they and their families receive quality services appropriate to their needs.

The autistic spectrum – a handbook 1999

Edited by Lesley Smeardon

Designed and produced by Ian Smythe

Ibis Creative Consultants Ltd

Published by

The National Autistic Society

Editorial note

The views expressed in this book are those of the individual contributors, and do not necessarily represent the policy of The National Autistic Society (NAS).

The NAS does not necessarily endorse the advertisements included in this publication.

While every effort has been made to ensure the accuracy of information given in this handbook, the NAS cannot accept responsibility for the consequences of any errors or omissions in that information.

In certain articles the masculine pronoun is used purely for the sake of convenience.

First published in Great Britain 1998 by The National Autistic Society,
393 City Road, London EC1V 1NG

ISBN 1 899280 02 2

Designed and typeset by Ibis Creative Consultants Ltd, Dulwich, London SE21 8EN
Tel: 0181 766 6280

Printed in Great Britain by Information Press Ltd.

Illustrations by Nancy Anderson

Registered charity number 269425

Contents

5   For professionals

5a   For teachers

5b   For GPs and other health professionals

6   Publications order form

7   Useful contacts

Introduction

Paul Cann, NAS Chief Executive

Our idea for creating this first edition of the autistic spectrum handbook was to bring together in one document information that spans the various needs of parents of children of all ages, people with the disability and professionals working in the field of autism.

While we have loosely grouped together articles that have been written specifically for a particular audience, we hope that most of you reading this will find the articles in all sections interesting.

For parents of young children we have included chapters about daily living skills and ideas for toys written by Jane Shields, Manager of the NAS EarlyBird project. Parents of older children may find the article about tackling depression by Jackie McCormick useful. And for people in the process of considering education for their child, the article by Rosemary Siddles and Mike Collins looking at education from pre-school through to university may be of interest.

For people with an autistic spectrum disorder, we have included chapters about finding a home, getting work and socialising; and for professionals, there are chapters about recognising the disability, teaching children with autism at both primary and secondary levels and on understanding the family.

The National Autistic Society was set up by parents and is governed by parents. Their concerns, rights and wishes will always be at the heart of the NAS and I hope the wider movement. My job as Chief Executive is to ensure that however large and diverse we become, we find ever more effective ways of reaching and supporting those, such as parents, who are directly affected by the challenge of autism. This Handbook is one more way in which we can work together to support each other. I hope you find it useful. Great thanks go to all the people who contributed articles to the Handbook.

SECTION I

The National Autistic Society (NAS)

Chapter 1

The National Autistic Society – from 1962 – 1999

On 23 January 1962 a group of parents, frustrated with the lack of provision and support for children with autism crowded into the living room of a North London home and formed The National Society for Autistic Children, later renamed The National Autistic Society. Their aim was to encourage a better understanding of autism and to pioneer specialist services for people with autism and those who care for them.

In those first few formative years of the Society's life, the hard work of parents laid much of the solid foundations of the present day Society and its activities, 37 years on. In the first ever newsletter produced by the Society four aims were outlined:

1 *To provide and promote a day and residential centre for the treatment and education of autistic children*
2 *To help parents; particularly by arranging meetings between them where they can exchange information*
3 *To encourage research into the problems of these children*
4 *To stimulate more understanding among the lay and medical public of these children's problems; and to tell them what can – and must be done to help the children lead normal lives.*

1 To provide and promote a day and residential centre for the treatment and education of autistic children

1962

In 1962 plans were in place to develop a school for children with autism. This was intended to act as a pilot scheme to demonstrate to local authorities what could and should be done for children with autistic spectrum disorders. In 1965, plans were made real when the first school in the UK for children with autism was opened (The Sybil Elgar School).

Today

Today, the Society not only runs six schools of its own, but its education advisors, together with Development Officers, provide assistance to local education authorities in the development of local provision. Because an autistic spectrum disorder is a lifelong disability, the NAS also runs, in addition to schools, a further education establishment, 17 adult centres and Prospects, a supported employment service for people with autistic spectrum disorders.

Support throughout life

The range of abilities, ages and needs of people with autism and Asperger syndrome is vast, and we constantly strive to develop and expand our current services in order to deliver the specialist help individuals need in order to live as full a life as possible.

Diagnosis and assessment

Despite an increased understanding of the autistic spectrum and the work of the NAS in educating professionals, a substantial proportion of parents still experience problems obtaining a clear diagnosis for their children. Confusion and delay over diagnosis conflict with the aim of starting appropriate treatment and education in the early years of life.

The Centre for Social and Communication Disorders was set up in 1991 by the NAS and was the first centre in the UK to provide a national diagnostic and assessment service for adults as well as children and adolescents with social and communication disorders.

The aims of the Centre are not just to focus on providing a diagnostic service but also to offer training in diagnostic procedures and to support the setting up of more centres of expertise in this field.

Education services

The NAS runs six schools for children of all ages with varying needs including more able students and those with high support needs arising out of challenging behaviours. Day and residential options are available which seek to offer flexible responses to the needs and circumstances of each person and his/her family. NAS schools follow the National Curriculum which has enabled students to transfer to mainstream schools where appropriate. Schools are approved by the Department for Education and Employment and supported by experienced professionals at a national and local level.

Class sizes are small (usually a maximum of six children) with the level of teaching and other support determined by individual need. In addition to schools, the NAS provides early intervention, advice and support to parents whenever possible.

SPELL – the NAS approach

The Society's approach to education aims to overcome or reduce the disabling effects of autistic spectrum disorders by providing a broad and balanced curriculum which gives extra help in the areas of communication and social skills as well as compensating for difficulties in imagination. The approach has been refined to recognise the individuality of each child or adult against a background of the condition of autistic spectrum disorders. The method of intervention is summarised as SPELL and comprises the inter-related elements of Structure, Positive approaches, Empathy, Low arousal and Links. It is a holistic approach which sees every child/adult as a unique individual albeit sharing similar experiences and difficulties.

Transition

Transition is a vital phase in the young person's life. Planning takes place from the age of 14 years and is kept under close review. All NAS schools have TAGs (Transition Action Groups) in place to ensure, as far as possible, the smoothest passage from school to the appropriate option for each individual student.

Further and higher education

A number of students move on to further and higher education and support is identified which will enable them to access and benefit from the opportunities offered. In addition, the NAS runs a further education college which links to vocational and educational facilities locally.

Services for adults

The NAS provides 17 residential and day services for adults with autistic spectrum disorders. There are a limited number of places on offer but the services cater for people throughout the whole autistic spectrum. This range includes residential and day provision in urban and rural settings offering flexible, specialist support to individuals with varying needs. These services also cater for individuals with Asperger syndrome and for people needing very high levels of staff support arising out of the nature of their autism and attendant difficulties. The aim of all services is to offer access to as full, enjoyable and meaningful a life as possible to each individual. Programmes are designed to offer additional help with difficulties in communication and social skills and to compensate for difficulties in imagination – all barriers to achievement of a full and enjoyable life.

Contacts

For details of NAS schools, adult centres and education advice:

Services Division
Church House
Church Road
Filton
Bristol
BS34 7BD
Tel 0117 987 2575
Fax 0117 987 2576

Employment

Prospects is a supported employment service run by the NAS and is the first in the country specifically designed to help people with autistic spectrum disorders find and retain work. The service works with employers like BT, Boots and Marks and Spencer to offer real jobs and real salaries to people with autistic spectrum disorders.

Contacts

For details of employment and related issues:
Prospects
The National Autistic Society Head Office
393 City Road
London   EC1V 1NG
Tel 0171 903 3597
Fax 0171 833 9666

Autism Services Accreditation Programme

The Autism Services Accreditation Programme is owned by the NAS but operates as an independent service to ensure consistent standards are achieved whether the care service is provided by the NAS, a local society, a local authority or another independent organisation.

The programme, the only one of its kind in the world as far as we are aware, provides an autism-specific benchmark of quality. Its aim is to assist, support and encourage all services for people with autistic spectrum disorders to attain and retain accreditation. This ensures that a service meets national standards and responds effectively and appropriately to the special needs of people with autism, both children and adults. At present there are over 100 separate services registered with the programme. For details of these services see Section VII - Useful contacts.

Contacts

The Autism Services Accreditation Programme
236 Henleaze Road
Bristol
BS9 4NG
Tel 0117 962 8962
Fax 0117 962 2220

2 To help parents; particularly by arranging meetings between them where they can exchange information

1962

In 1962 this was initially conducted with a few willing parents, acting as informal counsellors for other parents in the management of their children. Membership of the Society in 1962 stood at around 170 members.

Today

Today the Society's membership stands at 7,000 and is growing at a rate of 15% each year. The increase in members has naturally led to many more parents

Contacts

Membership enquiries
The National Autistic
Society Head Office
393 City Road
London
EC1V 1NG
Tel 0171 903 3563
Fax 0171 833 9666

getting together to provide mutual support by way of talks and sharing of information, social activities and awareness-raising among professionals and the general public. Many of these groups have formed into NAS Branches of which there are currently over 40. These Branches are situated throughout the UK stretching from the Highlands and Islands of Scotland to Devon. For more details of Branches, see Section VII.

Development and outreach

The NAS also has a growing development, outreach and training team that works with a range of statutory, voluntary and private sector agencies to help and encourage them to provide services for people with autistic spectrum disorders and their families via direct work or by providing training.

Development

Development Officers liaise with NAS Branches and local affiliated societies and organise workshops and meetings for parents. They are also the first point of contact for local authorities seeking to develop and expand services for people with autistic spectrum disorders. Each Development Officer covers a specific area of the country.

Outreach

Family support project workers seek to ensure support for families. Funded by local authorities, these workers provide liaison between the statutory sector, parents/carers and people with autism to try to ensure that they gain access to the support they need.

In addition, support is given to local societies who run family workshops. These groups and workshops provide a forum where parents can share experiences and discuss issues of importance to them. In this way, families are helped to overcome the isolating effects of autism.

Volunteering network

In 1997, the Volunteers Network was set up with help from a grant from The National Lotteries Charities Board. Two types of schemes were developed – Befriending and Parent to Parent.

Befriending

The befriending project recruits and vets volunteers to work with people with autistic spectrum disorders and their families. Volunteers provide 'time out' for all the family members by providing an extra pair of hands to help out. All volunteers receive training on the nature of autism, the effect on the family and interests and activities for people with autism.

Contacts

Development Officers

South West and Mid-Counties
Jan Snook
Tel 0117 987 2575

South East
Tracey Sellers
Tel 0171 903 3557

London and East Anglia
Greg Pasco
Tel 0171 903 3557

East Midlands and North East
Alan Bicknell
Tel 0115 911 3360

North West and West Midlands
Chris Barson
Tel 0115 911 3360

Wales
Delyth Elward,
Tel 01792 815915

Scotland
Gill West
Tel 0141 221 8090

Parent to Parent

The Parent to Parent scheme involves training parents of people with autistic spectrum disorders to help support other parents. Parent to Parent schemes vary from area to area as the needs of local communities are very different. Some examples include parents offering support at a local drop-in/telephone service on an individual basis – individual parent support attached to existing support groups – family to family support.

The NAS Volunteers Network provides free information, resources, training and support for those involved in both Befriending and Parent to Parent schemes.

Autism Helpline

The Autism Helpline, partially funded by the Department of Health, provides help, advice and support to people with autism and Asperger syndrome and their families. The Helpline is both a written and phone enquiry service.

Helpline workers with good local knowledge and access to regional networks provide callers with information and help on issues around autism, on the services available to families in their area, details of local authorities and other organisations specialising in autism operating in the area.

Contacts

The Volunteering Network
The National Autistic Society
Castle Heights
72 Maid Marian Way
Nottingham
NG1 6BJ

Tel 0115 911 3369
Fax 0115 911 3362

Email:
volunteers@nas.org.uk

Autism Helpline
The National Autistic Society Head Office
393 City Road
London
EC1V 1NG

Tel 0171 903 3555
(lines open
10 am – 11.30 am and
2 pm – 3.30 pm)

Email:
autismhelpline@nas.org.uk

3 To encourage research into the problems of these children

1962

In 1962 work was already underway to achieve this aim. Dr Lorna Wing (now working as a consultant at the NAS Centre for Social and Communication Disorders) sent out questionnaires to all members to find out how many of their children had been classified by local authorities under the Mental Health Act as ineducable.

Dr Wigley, the then medical officer for Middlesex, was a strong supporter of the NAS' work and argued for nursery education for autistic children to be provided by the Local Education Authority. Dr Wigley was also instrumental in getting the financial backing necessary to undertake the first epidemiological study of autism ever done by Victor Lotter. Lotter looked at the prevalence of Kanner's autism in every child of 8, 9 and 10 years in the old county of Middlesex.

Today

Today, the NAS encourages and supports various research projects in the hope that by focusing on scientific expertise and bringing together existing strands of research the key to the causes of autism will be found.

Tools for aiding diagnosis

Research looking at the reliability and validity of the Diagnostic Interview for Social and Communication Disorders (DISCO) used at The Centre for Social and Communication Disorders is nearing completion. DISCO is a new diagnostic interview schedule used for the diagnosis of disorders in the autistic spectrum. It collects information on a wide range of behaviours and developmental skills, enabling the clinician to diagnose across the autistic

Contacts

The Centre for Social and Communication Disorders
Elliot House
113 Masons Hill
Bromley
Kent BR2 9HT

Tel 0181 466 0098
Fax 0181 466 0118

spectrum. Once the research is complete, it is hoped to be able to make DISCO available to clinicians throughout the world.

The Centre also, from time to time, conducts monitoring and evaluation projects on the different approaches to autism.

The Autism Research Centre

The Autism Research Centre was established at the University of Cambridge in 1997 in partnership with the NAS, the University and Lifespan Healthcare NHS Trust. The Centre draws together the various strands of research being carried out at Cambridge University. Research projects being undertaken broadly fall into four areas: genetic, neurobiological, psychological and primary care.

In order to be relevant, research into the autistic spectrum must be informed by the needs of those affected and their families. The NAS is an essential partner in the Autism Research Centre with the role of ensuring that there is a patient/client group partnership in research.

4 To stimulate more understanding among the lay and medical public of these children's problems; and to tell them what can – and must be done to help the children lead normal lives

1962

Raising awareness among the general public and professional audience has always been considered of paramount importance to the Society. In 1962 work was already underway to raise the issues with parliamentarians and medical practitioners. In its first year the Society had managed to gain the support of MPs and raise the issue in the media through papers, such as the *Guardian* and *The Evening News*.

Today

Thirty seven years on, the Society works in many different areas to ensure that awareness of autistic spectrum disorders is increased among many different audiences, including the general public, local and central government, professionals working in the field, donors and sponsors. This is achieved though media work, fundraising, publications produced by the Society and responding to specific enquiries.

Information Centre

The Information Centre is for professionals with an interest in autism and related disorders, such as Asperger syndrome, whether they are students, researchers, voluntary organisations or NAS employees. The Centre responds to both written and telephone enquiries providing information and advice on all aspects of autism, NAS services and related topics.

The Centre has a library of materials on autistic spectrum disorders which can be viewed by appointment and holds a database of useful contacts and addresses of organisations and people throughout the world with an interest in autism. In addition the Centre produces a wide range of fact sheets, manages the information contained on the Society's Web site and monitors Internet information on autism throughout the world. The Centre can also carry out literature searches and produce customised reading lists using a computer database.

Training

NAS Training Services offers a range of training courses and conferences for professionals from all disciplines, parents and carers. Consultancy is available to local authorities and a range of agencies seeking to provide relevant services for people with autism and their families.

Contacts

The Information Centre
The National Autistic
Society Head Office
393 City Road
London
EC1V 1NG
Tel: 0171 903 3599
Fax: 0171 833 9666
Email:
informationcentre@nas.org.uk

Contacts

Training Services
The National Autistic
Society
Castle Heights
72 Maid Marian Way
Nottingham
NG1 6BJ
Tel: 0115 911 3363
Fax: 0115 911 3362
Email: training@nas.org.uk

Publications

The Publications Department at The National Autistic Society has one of the best lists on autism and Asperger syndrome in the country. It holds stocks of over 60 publications and these include papers and leaflets published by The National Autistic Society and many non-NAS publications written by well-known names in the field of autism and related disorders. In addition the Department produces the Society's magazine *Communication* and, in collaboration with Sage Publications, *autism*, the international journal.

Contacts

Publications Department
The National Autistic
Society Head Office
393 City Road
London
EC1V 1NG
Tel: 0171 903 3595
Fax: 0171 833 9666
Email:
publications@nas.org.uk

Press and PR

As well as working directly with the media the Department gets involved in a number of public relations activities. These include organising NAS involvement in conferences and exhibitions, where we can put our message across.

Taking advantage of opportunities within the political system of the UK and Europe is also important, in order to influence legislation that may affect people with autism and their families. The NAS has always worked closely with Government departments, striving to ensure they are conscious of the needs of people with autism and their families. The NAS is seeking to extend this area of its work to make sure the rights of people with autism are not overlooked or neglected.

Contacts

Press Office
The National Autistic
Society Head Office
393 City Road
London
EC1V 1NG
Tel: 0171 903 3593
Fax: 0171 833 9666
Email:
press@nas.org.uk

Looking forward

The tremendous achievement and growth of the Society in 37 years is testament to the work of the founding members of the organisation and the ongoing work of existing Board and staff members. Throughout the 37 years, the Society has been constantly revising the original four aims in line with its growth and achievements. In 1997 the NAS launched its 10 year vision, putting forward 40 aims for the forthcoming decade. These aims recognise the great inroads that have been made in awareness, provision, knowledge and expertise and seek to build on these significant successes.

For a full list of NAS contacts and other useful contact organisations, please see Section VII - Useful contacts - p161.

Chapter 2

The organisation of
The National Autistic Society

The Society is registered both with the Charity Commissioners and the Registrar of Companies. Its trusts and powers are laid down in its Constitution that states that the charity's objective is to provide education, treatment, welfare and care to people with autism and related conditions.

How the Society works

Membership
Our membership consists of 7,000 members – all are entitled to vote at the General Meeting of Members. This ultimately controls the Society's direction.

The members elect a Council of Members on an annual basis who represent the members' view at council level.

The Council
There are 42 voting members of Council who are either regional or national councillors. Regional councillors are elected by and represent members living in a particular region, while national councillors are elected by the whole membership and have a national mandate. In each year one-third of the councillors stand down.

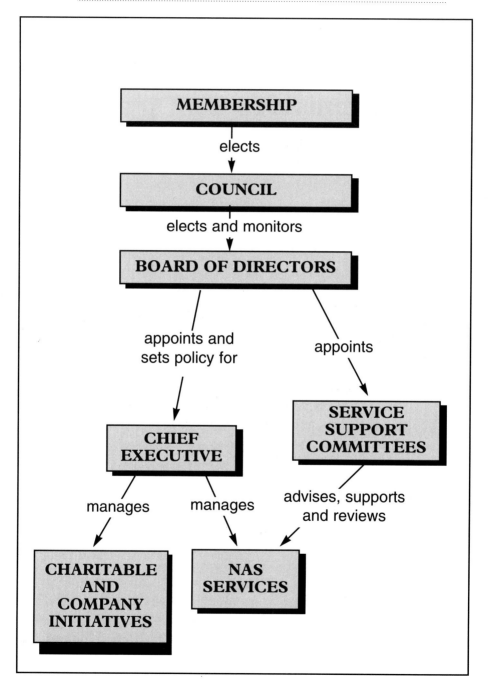

The Board of Directors

There are up to 12 Directors who are the legal trustees of the charity. The Directors are appointed by the Council at their annual election meeting. Four Directors stand down each year.

The Directors elect a Chairman who acts as the Chairman of the Society.

Chief Executive and Senior Management Team

The Senior Management Team members are Heads of Department and are accountable to the Chief Executive. The Chief Executive is accountable to the Board and the Board is accountable to the members of the NAS.

Branches

NAS Branches are part of the NAS and use the charity number. Branches are run by parents who join together to provide mutual support at a local level.

Affiliated societies

Since the early 1960s there has been an increasing number of independently registered charities who have the same basic aims as those of the NAS but who restrict their work to smaller geographical areas.

Most affiliated societies tend to concentrate their resources on either direct provision through schools and/or adult services, or on family support and the promotion of awareness among central and local government and the general public. More recently some of the larger direct service-providing local societies have started to develop their work into a broader base of activity.

At present, there are over 20 service-providing affiliated societies and over 30 non-service providing ones.

SECTION II

Autistic spectrum disorders

Chapter 3

Questions and answers about autistic spectrum disorders

Below are answers to some of the most frequently asked questions about autistic spectrum disorders. Please be aware that the answers we have given are generalised – questions surrounding the autistic spectrum do not present simple answers. Each individual with an autistic spectrum disorder presents a slightly different picture of the disability and it is impossible to explain each and every situation in short answers. However we hope that the answers we give here will provide you with a generalised explanation.

1 What is an autistic spectrum disorder?

An autistic spectrum disorder is a complex developmental disability that affects the way a person communicates and relates to people around them. The term autistic spectrum is often used because the condition varies from person to person; some people with the condition may also have accompanying learning disabilities, while others are much more able with average or above average intelligence. Asperger syndrome is a condition at the more able end of the spectrum. Also on the spectrum is Kanner syndrome, sometimes referred to as 'classic autism'. Despite all of the wide ranging differences, everyone with the condition has difficulty with social interaction, social communication and imagination (see also Question 6).

2 What is the difference between autism and Asperger syndrome?

Autism and Asperger syndrome are all part of the same autistic continuum and the differences between them relate more to degree than anything else. However, people at the more able end of the autistic spectrum, such as those with Asperger syndrome, tend to have average or above average intelligence and generally have fewer problems with language, often speaking fluently, though their words can sometimes sound formal or stilted.

3 What is the prevalence of autistic spectrum disorders?

In the latest research quoted by The National Autistic Society, figures for the prevalence of autistic spectrum disorders in the UK are 91 people in every 10,000. It is estimated that over 500,000 people in the UK have an autistic spectrum disorder.

These figures include people at the more able end of the spectrum who may not need specialist services and support but will still benefit from early recognition and sympathetic understanding of their special needs and unusual patterns of skill.

4 What is the sex ratio?

Boys are affected more often than girls. For 'classic' autism the sex ratio is four males to one female; for Asperger syndrome it is nine males to one female.

Myth	Autism is the result of emotional deprivation or emotional stress.
Fact	Autism is a complex developmental disability involving a biological or organic defect in the functioning of the brain.

5 Why are there more autistic males than females?

Unfortunately this is not known, though research suggests that genetic factors are involved. However, these ratio differences between males and females are helping with the investigations into the causes of autistic spectrum disorders.

6 What are the main criteria used for diagnosis?

All people with an autistic spectrum disorder have difficulties with social interaction, social communication and imagination. This is referred to as the triad of impairments.

- Social interaction (difficulty with social relationships, for example appearing aloof and indifferent to other people).
- Social communication (difficulty with verbal and non-verbal communication, for example not really understanding the meaning of gestures, facial expressions or tone of voice).
- Imagination (difficulty in the development of play and imagination, for example having a limited range of imaginative activities, possibly copied and used repetitively).

In addition to this triad, repetitive behaviour patterns are a notable feature and a resistance to change in routine.

7 What are the causes of autistic spectrum disorders?

The exact cause of autistic spectrum disorders is still not known but research shows that genetic factors are important. In some cases, autistic spectrum disorders may also be associated with conditions affecting brain development, such as maternal rubella, tuberous sclerosis and encephalitis.

Myth	Autism is a new phenomenon.
Fact	Centuries old myths of 'changeling children' could have been based on autistic children. The first detailed description of a child we now know was autistic was written in 1799.

8 What is the range of intellectual abilities?

From severe intellectual disability to average or above average intelligence.

9 What are the major differences in the development of language between people with intellectual disabilities with autism and without autism?

Language in autism is not only delayed, it is very disordered. Many people have immediate or delayed echolalia (mimicking speech), problems understanding what they hear, and a tendency to interpret language literally. In people with intellectual disabilities, language development is typically delayed but not disordered and does not show the unusual characteristics of autistic language development.

10 What is the best approach for developing language skills?

Programmes need to be based on individual strengths and needs. The most useful communication system for an individual with an autistic spectrum disorder is likely to incorporate signs, symbols, printed word, photographic or verbal communication, or any combination of these. It must be functional and consistent.

11 What is the NAS education philosophy?

The NAS has been at the leading edge of devising appropriate education programmes for children with autistic spectrum disorders. The Society's

Myth	A person with autism is ineducable.
Fact	With specialised education and structured support a person with autism can be helped to reach their full potential.

approach aims to overcome or reduce the disabling effects of autism by providing a broad and balanced curriculum which gives extra help in the areas of communication and social skills as well as compensating for difficulties in imagination.

The approach has been refined to recognise the individuality of each child or adult against a background of the condition of autism. The method of intervention is summarised as SPELL and comprises the inter-related elements of Structure, Positive approaches, Empathy, Low arousal and Links. It is a holistic approach which sees every child/adult as a unique individual albeit sharing similar experiences and difficulties.

12 How can problems with behaviour be managed?

The most effective behaviour management approach is a non-aversive one, ie one that does not use punishment or physical restraint. It is important to consider what the person with autism is communicating through the behaviour and act on that. Often the most effective management involves changing the events that occur before or after the behaviour. It is also important to create a relaxed environment to reduce stress and anxiety.

13 Are there some things that people with autistic spectrum disorders do brilliantly?

Some people with autism have exceptional skills in areas, such as music, art, memory, mathematics and motor skills. (For example being able to calculate the day of the week for any particular date.) However, these skills are not demonstrated by the majority of people with autistic spectrum disorders.

Myth	People with autism wish to avoid social contact.
Fact	People with autism are often keen to make friends but, due to their disability, find this difficult.

14 Do people with autistic spectrum disorders look different?

Autism does not affect the external appearance of a person with the condition. Their odd behaviour may sometimes cause them to stand out, particularly if these behaviours are self-stimulatory, such as rocking or flicking their fingers in front of their eyes. However, due to its general invisible nature it can be much harder to create awareness and understanding of the condition.

15 Is autistic spectrum disorder an emotional problem?

As mentioned in Question 7, genetic factors and conditions affecting brain development, are associated with the cause of autistic spectrum disorders. It is not caused by anything that parents do or do not do, or by any other aspects of the child's development.

16 Do children with the condition need to go to special schools?

It is most important that the educational programme developed for the child meets his or her needs and includes appropriate areas of learning.

For some children this is best managed with special support in a mainstream school; for others, a specialist school where the environment can be highly structured is more appropriate. Whatever the setting, the school needs to understand the nature of the child's disability and the implications this has for learning.

Myth	Autism is due to parental rejection or cold 'refrigerator' parents.
Fact	Autism has nothing whatever to do with the way parents bring up their children.

17 Do people with autistic spectrum disorders have physical disabilities?

Because the disorder can be associated with other conditions, some people with an autistic spectrum disorder do have physical disabilities. Sometimes autism is associated with a physical disorder, such as tuberous sclerosis and, in a substantial minority of people with autistic disorders, epilepsy is present. However, in the same way as in the general population, most people with the condition do not have a physical disability or any particular health problem and have a normal life expectancy.

18 Is there an effective treatment for autistic spectrum disorders?

An autistic spectrum disorder is a life-long disability and there is at present no one effective treatment that appears to work for everyone. However, the situation is not as bleak as this must, at first, appear. Given appropriate intervention early in life, specialised education and structured support can really make a difference to a child's life, helping to maximise their skills and achieve their full potential as adults.

For more information about recognising autism please refer to Section V, Chapter 15.

Myth	Autism is misunderstood genius.
Fact	While some people with autism have special abilities in narrow areas, this is not true for the majority.

Chapter 4

Resources

Items available from the Publications Department have a (P) listed after the title or if they are available from the Information Centre you will find a (I) listed after the title. To obtain copies, please refer to the Publications List (Section VI of this Handbook) or for articles available from the Information Centre please write to the Information Centre at The National Autistic Society, 393 City Road, London EC1V 1NG. Please note that book prices are correct at the time of print but these may be subject to change.

GENERAL INTRODUCTORY BOOKS ON AUTISM AND ASPERGER SYNDROME

Aarons, M and Gittens, T (1992) **The Handbook of autism: a guide for parents and professionals**. Routledge £13.99 plus p&p (P)
Practical in its approach, this book dispels many of the myths associated with the autistic condition and provides readers with information that makes sense.

Attwood T (1998) *Asperger's syndrome: a guide for parents and professionals* Jessica Kingsley £12.95 plus p&p (P)
Author of *Why does Chris do that?* Tony Attwood wrote this book to assist parents and professionals in the identification and treatment of children and adults with Asperger syndrome. The book provides a description and analysis of the unusual characteristics associated with Asperger syndrome and outlines practical strategies.

Baron-Cohen, S and Bolton, P (1995) *Autism: the facts.* Oxford University Press £8.99 plus p&p (P)
Recommended by the NAS as essential reading for all parents and carers of people with autism, this book explains autism in a way which is understandable, supportive and helpful.

Frith, U (1994) *Autism and Asperger syndrome* Cambridge University Press £15.95 plus p&p (P)
A clear and succinct presentation of the important findings relating to Asperger syndrome as a distinct variant of autism. Highly recommended to medical and behavioural scientists, parents, carers and professionals.

Gilpin, W (1993) *Laughing and loving with autism* Future Education Inc £6 plus p&p (P)
This is a collection of humorous stories written by parents, other family members, friends and teachers of children and adults from all over America.

Autism: the invisible children? (1996) The National Autistic Society £4.99 plus p&p (P)
The implications of current legislation for meeting the needs of children with autism.

Tantum, D (1991) *A mind of one's own* The National Autistic Society £1.99 plus p&p (P)
A helpful guide to the particular difficulties of the more able person with autism or Asperger syndrome.

Williams, D (1996) *Autism: an inside-out approach* Jessica Kingsley
£14.95 plus p&p (P)
This book by best selling author Donna Williams explores autism from the
inside. The author gives a personal insight into some of the behaviours
associated with the condition while also providing a wealth of helpful
suggestions and ideas.

Wing, L (1993) *Autistic spectrum disorders: an aid to diagnosis* The
National Autistic Society £1.99 plus p&p (P)
A description of the criteria used to diagnose people with autism. Essential
reading for parents, carers and other interested professionals. Also available
on tape.

Wing, L (1996) *The autistic spectrum: a guide for parents and
professionals.* Constable £16.95 plus p&p (P)
On its publication in 1971, Lorna Wing's book, *Autistic children* was
acclaimed as the definitive guide on autism. In this new book she develops
the themes of that book to include the latest developments in the field. This
new book describes what autism is, how to help those with the condition,
and the services available. This guide is invaluable for parents and anyone
working with people with autism.

Wing, L (1997) **'The history of ideas on autism: legends, myths and
reality'.** *Autism* Vol 1 (1) 13-23pp (I)

The InterACT Centre

c/o Hanwell Community Centre,
Westcott Crescent, London W7 1PD

Mission Statement

It is intended that a student leaves InterACT with a greater awareness of and practical ability in relating and interacting with other people.

● ● ● ● ● ● ●

Founded in 1994, *The InterACT Centre* is a non-residential further education college specialising in educating people with Autism and Asperger Syndrome.

For those students who find the demands of their local colleges as yet too great, we provide an alternative, a stepping stone. The learning is mostly practical and social skills are specific to the needs and relations of individual students. We offer a broad base of education.

Accredited learning includes: Key skills, ASDAN 'WorkRight', City and Guilds Craft Certificates and the RSA National Skills Profile.

The specific support available includes: explicit information, tutorials and action planning, small teaching groups, an understanding of adolescence, guidelines for behaviour, strategies for organising and planning, graduated supervision, graduation of the number and type of learning experiences and teachers who can entertain.

In 1995 the work of InterACT was inspected by The Further Education Funding Council and described as *"... particularly effective in enabling students to learn to interact appropriately with other people."* (FEFC report 1995.)

The InterACT Centre is also fully accredited by The National Autistic Society's Autism Network Quality Audit Scheme. *"The staff team have considerable theoretical knowledge and practical experience in the field of autism."* (Accreditation Report 1996.)

Principal: James E Graham
Tel: 0181 575 0046. E-mail: jamesg@dircon.co.uk

SECTION III

For parents

Clannalba House

Clannalba House, the base for the Society's Respite Care and Family Support Services, sits in its own pleasant grounds surrounded by beautiful countryside in the small hamlet of Lamington, near Biggar, in South Lanarkshire.

The facilities have been extended with the addition of a purpose built multi-sensory stimulation room and therapy pool and outdoor play area. There is separate accommodation to cater for both children and adults.

HOW TO ACCESS SERVICES

Clients will normally be referred through, and funded by, statutory services (Social Work, Health, Education).

The SSAC is able to advise parents on procedures to obtain a referral.

For further information, a referral form, or to arrange a meeting to discuss a client's needs please contact:

Family Centre Manager
The Scottish Society for Autistic Children,
Clannalba House, Lamington, Biggar, ML12 6HP.
Tel: 01899 850633
Fax 01899 850330

For further information on other autism-specific services, contact:
SSAC Headquarters, Hilton House, Alloa Business Park,
Whins Road, Alloa, FK10 3SA.
Tel: 01259 720044   Fax: 01259 720051

Respite Care
and
Family Support Centre
- A national resource

365 day service

—

Planned respite

—

Professional assessment of individual needs

—

Strategies reviewed in partnership with family and funding agency

—

Carer involvement where relevant

—

Integrated support systems

—

Educational and recreational

—

Welcoming and peaceful atmosphere

—

Emergency respite

—

Cost-effective care

**The
Scottish Society
for
Autistic Children**

Chapter 5

Education – from pre-school to university

Rosemary Siddles and Mike Collins
NAS Education Advisors

Education resources for school-aged children with autistic spectrum disorders are increasing slowly but surely. Each week we read in our newspapers and hear on television that there are no appropriate services for children with autistic spectrum disorders. This is simply not true. We do not pretend that there is enough provision, but a lot of what exists is very successful. The NAS is constantly seeking to improve and expand educational opportunities both by working with Local Education Authorities (LEAs) and setting up new schools.

The pre-school years

Unfortunately there is no statutory obligation on the part of education authorities to provide pre-school education. Recently there has been a move towards providing education for all children at four years old, but many children with autistic spectrum disorders would benefit from earlier education, at least part-time, at the point of diagnosis. Children with autistic spectrum disorders need to be actively taught the skills other children learn spontaneously through social interaction.

In some areas of the country, opportunities for education are provided by the Portage Education Programme (a teacher-led/parent education scheme). (See Chapter 23 for the address of Portage.) Other children attend child development centres (often for a variety of therapies), and some children attend specialist, mainstream nurseries, or crèches.

Parents often have to be pro-active in seeking out these facilities, and then find they have to inform the staff about the particular needs of their child. The NAS is keen to promote early intervention practice, and to this end has set up the EarlyBird project in South Yorkshire.

The EarlyBird Project

EarlyBird, a pilot project, situated in South Yorkshire aims to support parents in the period between diagnosis and school placement. The project helps parents to work with their child to help prevent the development of unsocial behaviours and to help the child learn how to communicate.

The project will provide a much needed good practice base from which many other projects of this kind can develop.

The primary years

Much Local Education Authority school provision for children aged between five and 11 years is linked to mainstream schools or schools for children with (moderate) learning disabilities.

Typically, such a specialist unit might have two classes, two teachers and three learning support assistants for 10 children; in other units the numbers of children might be greater. Good provision should be identifiable in terms of its adherence to the principles of SPELL. (See pull-out box overleaf.)

SPELL

At NAS schools and education centres every minute of every day is recognised as a learning opportunity. Where pupils are resident, education and care staff work together to design individual plans encompassing the 24 hours of the day. The SPELL approach has been developed in NAS schools to overcome or, at the very least, reduce the disabling effects of autism by providing a broad and balanced curriculum which gives extra help in the areas of impairment – namely, communication, social skills and imagination. SPELL stands for Structure, Positive, Empathy, Low Arousal, Links.

Structure enables the child to predict events. This helps to reduce the child's anxiety, providing an environment in which he/she feels safe enough to be able to concentrate on learning.

Positive approaches and expectations (not so high as to cause anxiety and not so low as to cause boredom) aim to enhance the child's self-confidence and self-esteem.

Empathy is necessary on the part of the teacher in order to see the world from the child's unique viewpoint; this then allows a learning programme to be designed using the way that child thinks and learns. This is essential as the child with autism is unable to see the world from anyone else's perspective but themselves.

To achieve a **Low Arousal** setting, which will create a reassuring atmosphere for children with autism, the classroom needs to be calm, allowing opportunities for relaxation and relief of tension. The NAS uses physical education and a variety of relaxation techniques to maintain an ordered and harmonious atmosphere. The style of the NAS approach is essentially non-confrontational and through supported rehearsal, pupils are encouraged to try new experiences thereby increasing their confidence.

It is vital that NAS schools communicate effectively with parents, other schools and agencies. In order to maximise the child's opportunities for inclusion in mainstream schools the NAS uses the National Curriculum and aims to maintain vital **Links** with parents, other professionals and the community.

In particular, such a school should have a well informed staff team which is well disposed to the particular needs of children with autistic spectrum disorders.

Choosing a unit linked to a mainstream school is sometimes a preferred option for the parents of young children. Where good practice exists there is a concentration on total staff training, a well informed Special Educational Needs Co-ordinator (SENco) and skilled teacher in charge of the special unit.

Difficulties can often be pre-empted by conscientious maintenance of a daily diary, agreement to review the Individual Education Plan every six weeks (each half-term) and a rigorous audit of the child's whole 24 hour programme at the Annual Review meeting.

Although once identified and diagnosed as having an autistic spectrum disorder a child is normally assessed and provided with a Statement of Special Educational Needs, this does not happen in all cases. In such a situation it may be necessary to highlight the child's needs with the Headteacher, the child's class teacher and the school SENco. As before, it will be necessary to maintain a high level of communication. In these circumstances parents sometimes seek out small LEA schools or independent schools where they feel their child will receive more individual attention. This can be successful, but again all the same principles of SPELL, and an excellent 'hotline' of communication apply. Always ensure that the receiving school knows all about your child's needs, before he or she arrives, so that the school is properly prepared.

Secondary education

The transition for children with autistic spectrum disorders from primary to secondary school may be very difficult. The child will be required to generalise, to reflect, to analyse, interpret and extrapolate: all processes which he/she will find hard or impossible to do.

Additionally the social and interactional sophistication of a busy secondary school may be too much for the child to tolerate. It is very typical for school placements to break down at this time, even though the child may be very intelligent, and may have coped well with primary school. Serious thought has to be given to the suitability of the school placement, be it special or mainstream and the child's overall needs, potential for learning, and happiness must be taken into account.

In the main, special units attached to secondary schools are not autism-specific, and cater for a variety of special needs. The SENco, as in primary schools, will organise the education for children with special educational needs and will help organise staff training.

Some children with autistic spectrum disorders manage in the mainstream setting, but the general impression is that it is a smaller number than those coping in primary school. Examinations are not automatically accessible to children with autistic spectrum disorders and teachers often seek to modify the exam conditions to provide access. There is some localised successful practice, and good examples are invariably supported by an advisory teacher service and/or education psychologist.

Further education

Once in 'learning mode' it is wise to keep the child with autistic spectrum disorders in education so that he/she can benefit as far as is possible. If your child is being educated in a special school, their place is usually available until the age of 19, and all schools are required to plan their education so that further education is distinctly different from the rest of the school's curriculum.

In the further education setting the young person will be taught personal, social and health education, daily living skills, community living skills, leisure and recreational skills, vocational studies and have the opportunity to integrate into college and work placements.

The role of the NAS

When a child has been unable to maintain a place in mainstream, LEA special provision or other independent provision, the parents and the LEA may seek more specialised resources and consider an NAS school.

Each of our schools has its own identity and provides for differing needs. The places range through from day schooling, day plus some occasional respite (perhaps a night or two a month) to weekly boarding, a few termly boarding places, and full-time residential schooling for 52 weeks a year. There are some children in each of the schools who have very challenging behaviour, and some who are very withdrawn.

In some cases a child may go to one of the NAS schools because he is 'looked after' (previously called 'in care') by the local authority and needs residence and schooling all in one package.

NAS schools operate just like other schools, with all the same legal requirements, including inspection by OFSTED and Social Services. All schools aim to provide and develop a range of services which are specialised, innovative, of high quality and well resourced: we continually seek to improve and provide models of good practice which are internationally recognised.

See Section VII - Useful contacts, for details of NAS establishments and other useful organisations.

The Essex Autistic Society

Registered Charity No. 1063717

Services for people with autistic spectrum disorder

School Services for children and young adults (aged 3-19). Weekly boarding available.

Doucecroft School,

163 High Street, Kelvedon, CO5 9JA
Tel: 01376 570060
Head Teacher: Kathy Cranmer

Residential Services for adults

Peldon Old Rectory, Ashton House and Seymour House,

Church Road, Peldon CO5 7PT
Tel: 01206 735206
Campus Manager: Len Vickerstaff

and at

71 Mersea Road

Colchester CO2 7QR
Tel: 01206 547588
Manager: Maureen Kerry

Day Services for adults

Jigsaw Centre

227 Gosbecks Road,
Colchester CO2 9JT
Tel: 01206 561877
Manager: Carol Gale

Head Office

12 St Peters Court, St Peters Street
Colchester CO1 1WJ
Tel: 01206 577678
Chief Executive: John M Jones LLB

Chapter 6

Daily living skills for young children

Dr Jane Shields
NAS EarlyBird Project Manager

Acquiring daily living skills

All children have to learn daily living skills as part of their development, gradually becoming independent in activities, such as eating, toileting, dressing and sleeping. All parents learn that the acquisition of these skills takes time and patience! When the child has an autistic spectrum disorder the tried and tested methods which parents (and grandparents) have used successfully with other children may not work. To understand why, it is necessary to appreciate the effects of the underlying triad of difficulties which constitutes autism; of the child's resistance to change, and of the possible accompanying sensory sensitivities.

General principles

Children with autistic spectrum disorders may take longer to achieve independence in daily living skills and this development may follow a different pattern. But children with autistic spectrum disorders can be helped if, as parents, we observe the preferences of our individual child and follow some general principles.

1 Be aware of the underlying differences

Children with autism have difficulties in the areas of social interaction, social communication and imagination. They may show obsessive and repetitive behaviour. They may have tantrums which do not appear to be caused by factors commonly known to produce tantrums in other young children. Rather than simply noting the child's observed (and sometimes problematic) behaviours, it is more helpful to look for possible underlying causes and triggers for these behaviours – and for their difficulties in mastering the acquisition of daily living skills.

Resistance to change

The world can be a confusing place for people with autism and they show a compensating preference for sameness and routine. This may show itself in the child who plays continually with the same cars, lining them up on the same window ledge – or in the child who is reluctant to make the change from wearing a nappy to using the toilet. When changes occur in daily routines, tantrums may result and the child may resist any disturbance of established patterns of activity. Since the acquisition of daily living skills inevitably involves adults imposing change on the child, careful planning will be necessary to overcome the child's resistance to change.

Preference for routines

The positive side of resistance to change is that people with autism enjoy routines! Daily living skills will be acquired more easily if you build up independence skills gradually, using consistent routines which help your child to understand and remember what is required.

Poor response to social praise

All children need persuasion to learn independence in daily living skills and normally developing children can usually be successfully encouraged with social praise, such as smiles and 'good boy' or ' well done'. The underlying social deficits of autism mean that social praise is less likely to be appreciated by the child with an autistic spectrum disorder and other, more tangible rewards may be needed in order to motivate your child to learn new skills.

2 Allow for sensory sensitivities

Children with autism often show unusual responses to sensory stimuli: to the sensations of sound, touch, taste, smell and vision. They may experience sensations as more or less intense than we do and may therefore either over or under-react. Fear of intense sensory stimuli may cause the child to become anxious or fearful in anticipation. Daily living skills involve many sensations: the taste and texture of food; the darkness of the bedroom; the sound of a flushing toilet; the touch of a comb or nail scissors; the smell of soap or toothpaste.

3 Help your child to understand what you want

Adjust your language

The language you use needs to be at an appropriate level for your child. Children with autism are often slow to develop understanding and may need longer to process what they hear. Use your child's name first, to get his or her attention. Keep your sentences simple and concentrate on key words. Give instructions one at a time and use the same words each time you tell your child to do a particular action or sequence (such as getting dressed or coming to the table). Be positive: always tell your child what to **do** not what **not** to do. Give instructions in the order in which they are to be carried out – eg not 'you can have a story when you've got your pyjamas on and have been to the toilet', but 'Toilet – pyjamas on – then story'.

Use visual structure

Children with autism are visual learners: they are helped to understand and learn new skills by cues which they can see. Many daily living skills involve sequences of actions and these can be shown visually by using pictures (or symbols). Displaying the sequence helps the child to see what is expected (eg 'clothes off' – 'bath' – 'book' – 'sleep'). Picture cues also allow your child to see when each stage has been achieved (a picture can be turned over or flapped down when 'finished') and to develop independence in following the desired sequence. If there are elements in a daily living sequence which your child dislikes, a picture sequence also allows you to show the child the motivator which lies ahead (eg the 'book' after 'bath' in the sequence above).

4 Use motivating reinforcers

We all need to be motivated to make the effort of learning new skills. Children with autism are no exception, but the motivator that persuades them to make the effort may not be our choice. In choosing a 'reward' for your child you should use your knowledge of the child's preferences. One child may learn to get dressed for the reward of listening to a favourite tape; another may make the effort to eat so as to be allowed to play with his collection of twigs!

5 Plan small steps

All children are helped to learn new skills if these are broken down into small steps so that the child can learn one step at a time, rather than being faced by a seemingly impossible sequence of actions. When toilet training your child, you would not expect the child to be able to make the change from wearing a nappy to using the toilet independently, all at once. The child with autism may need to learn one very small step at a time, and progress may be slow – but then the child may suddenly take a step forward. The learning pattern of children with autism is less predictable than that of normally developing children.

6 Be consistent

When you introduce new daily living skills to the child with autism you are inevitably introducing change, which your child is likely to resist. It will be very important to persevere – so do not begin a new skill (such as toilet training) until you are ready to continue your efforts. The child may show difficult behaviour at first but your persistence will be rewarded. It will also be very important to be consistent in the demands which you make of your child: do not remove a nappy one day but allow them to wear it again the next. Whatever strategy (and accompanying language) you decide on, be sure that everyone who will be involved with your child uses the same ones, consistently.

7 Use 'backward chaining' to teach daily living sequences

Many daily living skills involve the child learning a sequence of actions. These should be broken down into small steps to help your child learn. To avoid the child experiencing failure in this learning a process called 'backward chaining' can be used. This involves helping your child to complete the last step of the sequence only, at first. If you are teaching your child to put a jumper on, you could put the jumper on but leave the child to pull it down (using the physical prompt of your hand over his at first). Once the child can do this unaided, show him how to put his second arm into a sleeve, and pull the jumper down. Then gradually teach him to do more and more steps until finally no help is needed. Teaching the steps of the sequence 'backwards' in this way means that your child learns the full sequence gradually, without ever making an error.

Eating

Children with autism are not the only ones to be faddy eaters! All children have to go through the stages of weaning from milk to a mixed diet, and they gradually learn the skills (and socially acceptable behaviour) of feeding themselves. Sensory sensitivities may interfere with the introduction into the child's diet of a range of foods – some children resist hard or lumpy foods; others will only eat food of a certain colour or shape; some prefer to eat only dry food, or only cold food. If you are aware of the underlying cause of these unusual preferences, you can more easily make gradual changes to your child's diet. The child's resistance to change may interfere with the introduction of new foods, or with the progress from feeder cup to glass and from baby spoon to knife and fork. Once again, these skills are best handled by making gradual changes and by using a motivating 'reward' to encourage your child to learn new skills.

Sleeping

The child with autism may have an unusual sleep pattern. Some children appear to need little sleep and others refuse to sleep alone. The underlying causes of difficult behaviours relating to sleep may be unusual sleep requirements; or sensory sensitivities (fear of the dark; hypersensitivity to household or external noises). Resistance to change may make your child reluctant to change from sleeping near you to sleeping alone in a room. It may well be necessary to teach sleeping skills and/or to modify your child's room so that they can be safely left to play there if awake during the night. The child's like of routines can be used in establishing a bedtime routine which minimises stimulation and helps them settle down to sleep. Fear of the dark may be helped by a nightlight; the disturbance of intermittent noises may be compensated for by playing a quiet tape under your child's bed. The change to light summer nights and mornings can be minimised by the use of thick curtains or blinds. Some children will be soothed by being 'swaddled' in bedclothes. For a child who insists on a parent sleeping next to him or her, use gradual change to move a little further away from your child's bed each night (put a lilo on the floor) until he/she will settle without you present.

Toileting

As with eating, all children take some time to learn independence in the skills of toileting. In addition, these skills require the child to be physically and mentally mature enough before the 'right time' for training comes. The child needs to become aware of bowel and bladder function; to be able to control the production of urine and faeces; and to communicate the need to use the toilet. The child with autism may reach the stage of readiness for toilet training later than a normally developing child. In addition, there may be resistance to the changes involved in moving from wearing a nappy to using a potty or toilet – a nappy can feel very comfortable and some children use their newly acquired control to avoid urinating until their trainer pants are replaced by the familiar nappy. As with any child, you will need to watch your child to see when the toilet is most likely to be needed, and to put him/her on the potty or toilet regularly. (For some children it may be easier to make one change; from nappy to toilet, rather than two changes, from nappy to potty to toilet.) Use an associated motivating 'reward' (something the child enjoys) to associate with successful urination or defecation in the appropriate place. Ignore 'mistakes' and reward successes. Be aware that some children may have sensory sensitivities related to toileting, such as fear of the noise of the toilet flushing or fascination with water.

Hygiene

The daily living skills which involve hygiene include washing and bathing; teeth and hair brushing; and cutting nails and hair. As with toileting, these skills are most easily taught if broken down into small steps but there may well be problems due to underlying causes. Water may be a source of fascination, or of fear. The child may be hyper- or hypo-sensitive to water temperature and may not understand the significance of hot and cold taps. The touch sensations caused by hair combing or cutting may be unpleasant for your child, as may the feel of having nails brushed or cut. To overcome these factors, try to discover things which your child enjoys and finds relaxing that can be linked with, or incorporated into, hygiene routines. Try bubbles and coloured or scented bath essence. Find motivating toys for the bath. Play a favourite tape while your child is in the bathroom. Have a motivating 'reward' visible, and tell your child that it will follow a feared activity (such as nail cutting). Find a friendly hairdresser who will visit your home, then let your child see a parent or sibling have their hair cut first, with a favourite video playing to calm them.

Dressing

Use small steps and backward chaining to teach your child to get dressed independently. Use visual cues – perhaps a 'timetable' of pictures or symbols to help your child to learn the sequence of dressing (and to know what motivating activity will follow when dressing is 'finished'). Resistance to change may mean that your child insists on wearing the same tee-shirt every day; or on wearing a scarf and gloves long after the snow has gone. Sensory sensitivities may explain why your child finds certain clothes uncomfortable; labels are a frequent cause of irritation.

Some children prefer (or object to) a certain colour, which can affect choice of clothes. Some dislike wearing shoes (or clothes!) and like to remove them. A firm and consistent approach will be necessary in teaching your child that it is not acceptable to strip off in public and that it is not safe to run outside without shoes. It may be helpful to start by insisting that shoes (and clothes) must be worn before your child is allowed access to a motivating activity such as the garden swing.

Chapter 7

Ideas for toys and leisure activities

Dr Jane Shields
NAS EarlyBird Project Manager

We have compiled a list of toys and equipment that many parents have found popular with their autistic children in the past. You may find some suit your child better than others and you, more than anyone else, will know your child's specific likes and dislikes. The following is intended as a guide or as a starting point for you to explore further.

Toys which are visually interesting

"Children with autistic spectrum disorders tend to prefer toys that involve visuo-spatial skills such as shape and colour matching, jigsaw puzzles or constructional materials."

Here is a brief list of some of the sorts of toys they may enjoy.
- Bubbles (bubble blowers)
- Colour torch (Early Learning Centre)
- Shape and colour matching, or sorting toys
- Formboards and jigsaws
- Jack-in-the-box, or Tomy 'pop-up-pirate'
- Duplo, lego, and other construction toys
- Early Learning Centre 'Marble Run'
- Various train toys (especially Thomas the Tank Engine): from push 'n' go versions to full train sets (eg Brio)
- Activities for drawing, colouring and painting (including

'Magnasketcher')
- Picture-word lotto
- Videos – especially Thomas, Pingu and Disney.

Books

Rather than just a book with plain text, try looking at some of the following for variation.
- Board books
- Books with flaps
- Touchy books
- Word books (often with photos of familiar objects)
- Usborne *First 100 words* and *First 1,000* words books
- Dr Seuss books
- Factual books
- Puzzle books

Physical activity toys

"It is useful to encourage physical activities that are enjoyable without the need for imagination and understanding and use of language. Physical exercise is reported to diminish inappropriate behaviour and such activities are also helpful for improving problems of motor co-ordination."
Here are some ideas as to the sorts of toys they may enjoy.
- Swing
- Slide
- Trampoline
- Rocking horse
- Climbing frame
- Football
- Ride-on toys: bikes, tractor etc
- Paddling pool
- Sand pit
- Basket ball net

Remember that, as for most activities, supervision is important. This is particularly true with activities like trampoline and climbing frames.

Games to play with other people

"It is worth trying to engage the children in simple games. Some children reach the level at which they can play picture-matching games or board games, such as ludo or snakes and ladders. Some of the most able learn to play chess and do well because of their excellent visuo-spatial memories. Board games give the opportunity of teaching the concept of winning or losing."

- Tapes of singing and dancing games
- Picture lotto games
- Snap
- Skittles
- *Connect 4 – Four in a row*
- WHOT!
- Guess who?
- Snakes and ladders
- Ludo
- Chess

Many of the above toys are available from Early Learning Centre shops or from their catalogue (Tel: 0990 352352).

Computer software

"Computers and computer games are particularly fascinating but can become a dominant obsession so parents should, from the start, impose clear limits on the time allowed."

- Early programmes, such as *Make it happen: Jump ahead toddlers* (Knowledge Adventure)
- Character software, such as Pingu; Dr Seuss Living Books; Disney Magic Artist
- Software to develop vocabulary, such as 'Word Rescue' (Apogee Software); Talking Alphabet (Sherston)
- Factual software, such as: Microsoft Magic School Bus; Encarta

- Future Horizons, 720 N Fielder, Arlington, Texas 76012, USA publish a book: *Point, click and learn* which lists and describes software for children and adults with autistic spectrum disorders. Cost $19.95 and $10.00 for postage.

All quotes are from ***The autistic spectrum: a guide for parents and professionals*** by Lorna Wing. Available from the NAS Publications Department (0171 903 3595) price £16.95 + £2.50 p&p.

Top 20 games

A survey (in the summer term) asked parents of primary aged children at a National Autistic Society school what were their children's preferred leisure activities. Here are the 20 favourites, in order of popularity:

1   swings, slides, climbing frames, park

2   swimming

3   seaside, paddling pool, water play

4   videos, television

5   eating out

6   walking in woods

7   music, singing

8   computer

9   riding bike, go-cart

10 trampoline, bouncing

11 funfairs, rides

12 books, comics

13 animals

14 sports

15 travel by car, bus

16 trains, Thomas the Tank Engine

17 sand

18 drawing, colouring

19 games: snap, *Connect 4*

20 running and chasing.

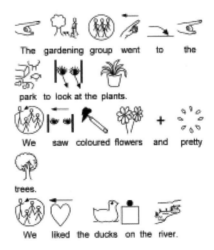

Chapter 8

Growing up – tackling depression

Jackie McCormick, Manager of Gloucestershire Group Homes

Introduction

The information contained in this article is presented in a factual and honest way. It is very important to stress that not all people with Asperger syndrome will experience periods of depression or become particularly anxious and disturbed in relation to how they view their personal situation.

However, people with Asperger syndrome are perhaps more likely to suffer from depression than the rest of the population (perhaps up to 15 per cent – Tantum 1991). These people may require varying degrees of treatment according to the severity of the depression. This article has been put together to try to help those families who believe that depression may be a problem for their son or daughter.

Recognising depression

As a young child, the person with Asperger syndrome is not necessarily so aware of their difficulties. It is not until adolescence and on into adult life that their heightened awareness raises the issue of distinct differences from their peer group. During adolescence they may become more interested in social activities and try extremely hard to make friends and be like other teenagers.

The reality for some is that through their attempts, they become the targets for ridicule and exclusion. Time and time again they misinterpret the social rules and fail to understand how others may view their behaviour as strange or odd.

Many individuals have described the constant feeling of failure and fear, which then results in emotions of anger at the difficulties they have in, as one person describes, 'being able to tune in'.

It is therefore understandable if experiencing some or all of the above difficulties that individuals with Asperger syndrome may suffer from a form of depression at some point during their lives. One young man aged 24 describes how pointless at times he believes his life to be. 'Every time I take the step to do something to improve my life, I just keep getting it wrong'.

Many individuals express the despair they feel at not being able to make friends, especially when it comes to forming relationships with a 'girlfriend or boyfriend'. Often parents and professionals will describe situations where the person with Asperger syndrome has asked to be taught how or what to do. 'Just tell me the right things to say that will help me get a girlfriend'.

Factors that may cause depression

Unfortunately there are many situations that people with Asperger syndrome find frightening and extremely confusing. These can range from social gatherings, working environments, college etc. All of these situations have the potential of increasing the individual's awareness of how different their personal situation is to that of others and result in a reactive depression.

Issues that may affect the young person with Asperger syndrome
*   Heightened awareness of differences with peer group
*   Inability to form successful relationships
*   Loneliness
*   Difficulties with their sexuality
*   Constant feelings of failure

- Extreme anxiety levels
- Pressure to take part in social activities, such as accessing college, work, social events.

This list is not exhaustive, and there may well be situations that are extremely stressful for the individual but we easily fail to recognise.

Signs and symptoms of reactive depression

- Frustration
- High anxiety
- Anger
- Withdrawal/isolation
- Self critical
- Changeable mood swings
- Low motivation
- Increased obsessional interests
- Increased ritualistic behaviour

It is important to realise that the depression may become so severe that it results in extreme anxiety states and the individual may feel or threaten suicidal acts.

If an individual has severe depression the following signs may also be evident:

- lack of appetite
- erratic sleep patterns
- complete withdrawal from any activity
- extreme aggression
- weight fluctuation
- skin abnormalities
- alcoholism
- suicidal thoughts and actions.

As described earlier, people with Asperger syndrome have many experiences that they have to understand/make sense of. If they are feeling confused, frightened or angry they may not always have the ability to express this in a way that others will understand. This being partly due to the difficulties they may have in verbal and non-verbal communication.

It is often the case that GPs and psychiatrists who have limited experience of the condition will fail to see the signs and refuse treatment. An example of this being when a young man was taken to the local GP by staff from his Group Home. (In order to gain access to the local psychiatric team, a referral is required from the GP.)

Unfortunately, the GP believed that due to the individual's ability to discuss a variety of topics at great length with no expression of 'feeling low' or clear suicidal thoughts, then he could not diagnose any form of depression and suggested the staff were being over-cautious. Unfortunately, the individual's depression became extreme and culminated in an attempted suicide which then resulted in a period of hospitalisation.

Please note, this is not the case for all people but it is necessary to recognise how difficult it can be to make the diagnosis, particularly if the individual is unable to express how they are feeling.

Ways to help

Once the signs and some of the causes of depression in individuals with Asperger syndrome are recognised, much can be done to support and hopefully prevent the individual from suffering depression in the future.

Suggestions of support

Here are some ideas of possible ways to support the person who has suffered from depression in order to help prevent a future recurrence.

- Increase security by providing routine, structure and consistency.
- Reduce anxiety by modifying the environment so that the individual can cope better with their surroundings.
- Provide emotional support.
  Often it is important just to let the individual know that you are there if they need you. You may just need to be around in the background reducing environmental pressure.
- Assess the boredom factor of the individual's life.
- Review the exercise routine and the person's diet. It may be that a more balanced diet would help to maintain a nutritional balance.
- Teach relaxation techniques that are relevant to the individual.

- Consider counselling. This should be provided by someone experienced in Asperger syndrome and if structured correctly, can be effective.
- Psychiatric/psychological intervention.
- Hospitalisation. This will only be necessary in extreme circumstances and hospitalisation is very rare.

Other support

Support groups

There are a growing number of support groups for both the person with Asperger syndrome and their parents/carers. Please contact your local NAS Branch or local society to find out what is available in your area. Further details of Societies/Branches can be found in Section VII - Useful contacts.

The Internet

A few individuals have reported how access to the Internet and the availability of autobiographies have helped considerably in helping them to come to terms with, not only their Asperger syndrome, but in learning effective ways to manage their lives, thus reducing the likelihood of depression. A list of web sites for people with autistic spectrum disorders can be found in Section VII - page 168.

One young lady explains that it wasn't until she started making contact with others that she realised it wasn't all her fault that the children at school bullied and teased her. It was because of the difficulties she experienced due to her disability.

This contact with others and her growing knowledge of the diagnosis also gave her the confidence to explain to family and friends the things that upset her and made her frightened and confused.

'At last I can stop trying to be like everyone else and enjoy my own life. I don't need your kind of friends because my friends are my books and my hamsters. I don't have to be embarrassed about this any more.'

Summary

There are no easy answers to managing depressive illness in people with Asperger syndrome, particularly when it can be so difficult to detect. As mentioned earlier, due to the limitations in self-awareness and communication, the individual may be unable to express fully their experiences of frustration and distress.

It is therefore important to view sudden changes in behaviour, sleep patterns, anger and withdrawal as possible signs that a depressive illness is affecting the person with Asperger syndrome.

The earlier this can be detected, the earlier the appropriate treatment and support can be sought to minimise the effects and prevent the individual from losing control over their lives.

Chapter 9

Resources

Items available from the Publications Department have a (P) listed after the title or if they are available from the Information Centre you will find a (I) listed after the title. To obtain copies, please refer to the Publications List (Section VI of this Handbook) or for articles available from the Information Centre please write to the Information Centre at The National Autistic Society, 393 City Road, London EC1V 1NG. Please note that book prices are correct at time of print but these may be subject to change.

EDUCATION

Atherton, G (1989) *In special need: a handbook for parents and young people in Scotland with special educational needs*. HMSO.
Many young children and young people require additional or specialist help with their education because of learning difficulties, various disabilities and emotional and other problems. This handbook explains to parents the very important role they can play in co-operation with professional staff in working out the kind of help or support their child needs and interprets the legislation as it relates to Scotland.

Cowderoy, J (1995) **How to choose a school for a child with Asperger syndrome**. The National Autistic Society (I)
Finding a suitable school for a child with Asperger syndrome can be a time-consuming and expensive exercise. This updated advice sheet suggests some resources and sources of information that may help parents build up a list of potentially suitable schools.

Department for Education (1994) *Special educational needs: a guide for parents* DfEE Publication Centre, PO Box 2193, London E15 2EU

Friel, J (1995) *Young adults with special needs: assessment, law and practice*. Jessica Kingsley
A handbook for parents, carers and people working with young people with special needs and covers the assessment of and procedure for young adults with special needs. Includes information on the 1992 Further and Higher Education Act and the 1993 Education Act.

Jordan, R and Powell, S (1995) **'Factors affecting school choice for parents of a child with autism'**. *Communication* winter. (I)
The authors details a range of considerations which they believe parents need to bear in mind when choosing a school for a child with autism.

Jordan, R and Powell, S (1995) *Understanding and teaching children with autism*. Wiley £18.99 plus p&p (P)
Offers practical guidance for parents, teachers and other professionals working with children with autism on ways of overcoming and avoiding the problems that the triad of impairments can cause.

Jordan, R and Powell, S (1997) *Autism and learning: a guide to good practice*. David Fulton £13.99 plus p&p (P)
This publication demonstrates how a cognitive perspective on the way in which individuals with autism think and learn may be applied to particular curriculum areas.

Kemp, D *Children and young persons with special educational needs – assessment and recording*. The Scottish Office Education and Industry Department, Area 2A (West), Victoria Quay, Edinburgh EH6 6QQ.

The National Autistic Society (1998)*The autistic spectrum – a parent's guide* £2 including p&p (P)
This pack has been put together specifically for parents and carers of children with autistic spectrum disorders. It is designed to answer some of the questions you may have about how best to help your child and throughout you will find pointers as to where you can go for further help on specific issues.

The National Autistic Society *The education of children with autism* Free information sheet (I)

The National Autistic Society (1998) *Schools, units and classes for children with autism* £2.99 plus p&p (P)
A list of specialist schools and units in the UK catering for children with autism.

The National Autistic Society (1997)*Timetable for autism* 50p plus p&p (P)
An overview of educating children and young people with autistic spectrum disorders.

Network '81 (1994) *Statements: a handbook for parents in England and Wales.*
A step-by-step guide to statementing for parents. This second edition has been updated to cover the 1993 Education Act Part III and Code of Practice. Available from Network '81, 1-7 Woodfield Terrace, Stansted, Essex CM24 8AJ. Price £5 including p&p.

The Scottish Office Education Department *A parent's guide to special educational needs* Room 4/20, New St Andrew's House, Edinburgh EH1 3SY.

Sissons, M (1996) *Special educational needs: a guide for parents.* RADAR. The purpose of this booklet is to ensure parents are aware of issues surrounding the education of disabled children, special educational needs (SEN) and the duties placed on local education authorities concerning the provision of educational services for disabled children. This booklet will also help to establish the courses of redress for children when things go wrong. Available from RADAR, 12 City Forum, 250 City Road, London EC1V 8AF. Price £2.50 including p&p.

Skill: National Bureau for students with disabilities. (1997) *Opportunities in education and training for young people with disabilities or learning difficulties after 16.*
Gives easy-to-understand, jargon-free information abut educational and training opportunities for young people with disabilities or learning difficulties after 16. The material covers staying on at current school, further education colleges, specialist colleges, higher education, vocational training, sources of further help and guidance, funding, benefits, useful contacts and publications. Skill's information service telephone number is 0171 978 9890 (1.30 – 4.30 pm Monday to Fridays). Skill, 336 Brixton Road, London, SW9 8RR.

DAILY LIVING SKILLS

Dickenson, P and Hannah, L (1998) *It can get better* The National Autistic Society £5 plus p&p (P)
This slim volume gives parents some useful hints and tips on how to deal with some of the more difficult behavioural problems their young child may have. Chapters deal with toileting, sleep disturbances, eating, tantrums, self-injury, destructive and obsessional behaviour. The book is aimed at parents with young children with autistic spectrum disorders.

Leicestershire County Council and Fosse Health Trust (1998) *Autism: how to help your young child*. The National Autistic Society £8.99 plus p&p (P)
This practical booklet is divided into three areas where difficulties may arise for a child with autism: social interaction, communication and imagination. The booklet includes an index of pen-pictures to help parents find their child among the examples and directs them to the relevant section. Each section is then divided into 'What to look out for' followed by 'Things to try' to help the child's behaviour.

Schopler, E (Ed) (1995) *Parent Survival Manual: a guide to crisis resolution in autism and related development disorders* Plenum Press £21.99 plus p&p (P)
This publication is the joint work of parents and professionals. It is a collection of ingenious solutions that parents have developed as responses to

the continual challenges of living with autism. Staff of Division TEACCH at the University of North Carolina, have accompanied each solution with a commentary that analyses why and how it works. The book offers quick reference to solutions of the most difficult behaviour problems such as aggression, communication, preservation, play and leisure, eating and sleeping.

Zarkowska, E and Clements J (1994) *Problem behaviour and people with severe learning disabilities: the STAR approach* Chapman & Hall
A practical manual for care staff, teachers – anyone engaged in the long-term resolution of behaviour problems.

AUTISM AND ADULTHOOD

Attwood, T (1993) *Why does Chris do that?* The National Autistic Society £3.99 plus p&p (P)
Some suggestions regarding the cause and management of the unusual behaviour of children and adults with autism and Asperger syndrome.

Howlin, P (1996) *Autism: preparing for adulthood* Routledge £14.99 plus p&p (P)
The author focuses on adults with autism and their families. By using information from research studies and treatment programmes, it will provide a practical resource for parents, carers and autistic people themselves. The author discusses problems and solutions related to educational and occupational attainments and ways of coping with psychiatric and other difficulties and fostering independence in later life.

Morgan, H (1996) *Adults with autism: a guide to theory and practice* Cambridge University Press £24.95 plus p&p (P)
From childhood services to adult provision, the needs of an individual develop and change, yet the literature addressing specific adult requirements is scarce. This volume sets out to fill this gap and provides practical help and guidance specifically for those caring for the growing recognised population of adults with autism.

Mortlock, J (1993) *The socio-sexual development of people with autism and related learning disabilities* The National Autistic Society £1.25 plus p&p (P)
A practical guide to the development and management of appropriate socio-sexual behaviour in people with autism and related learning disabilities.

The Inge Wakehurst Trust (1991) *Adolescents and adults with Asperger syndrome* £4.99 plus p&p (P)
Covers a range of issues related to the lives of adolescents and adults with Asperger syndrome including the problems of diagnosis, a parent's viewpoint, work experience and independent living.

The Inge Wakehurst Trust (1994) *Adolescents and adults with autism* £4.99 plus p&p (P)
This collection addresses a wide range of issues related to adults and adolescents with autism including: the transition from school to adult provision; self-care and living skills; occupational opportunities and work experience; understanding challenging behaviour; and matching services to needs.

Schopler, E and Mesibov, G (Ed) (1983) *Autism in adolescents and adults* Plenum
Provides an overview of the historical context of the autistic disorder, plus a series of chapters on the disabilities and needs presented by people with autism and their families.

0151 931 5366

To meet the needs of people with Autism, their families and carers throughout the North West by providing a comprehensive range of services which are personal, professional and innovative.

Autism Initiatives Registered Charity Number: 702632

SECTION IV

For people with autistic spectrum disorders

Chapter 10

Access to independent living

Alan Bicknell, NAS Development Officer for East Midlands and North East Region

Finding a home

Introduction

For most of us there comes a time in our lives when, for whatever reason, we make the decision to leave the family home. We may be starting a family of our own, going to college, moving to a new job or simply leaving the 'nest' to become more independent.

For many it is a big step and not easy, with pitfalls all along the way. As a person with autism or Asperger syndrome, it may be more complicated for you.

In order to find the right kind of home for you, you must be as well informed and prepared as possible in knowing what housing options are available and in understanding the process you use to access these services. In this article we have given you some starting points in finding the right home.

Firstly, the principles!

As a person with autism or Asperger syndrome, you have a right to:

- an ordinary pattern of life within the community
- be treated as an individual
- additional help and support in developing your maximum potential.

You should have as much freedom as anyone else to choose where you live and who you live with.

Housing – the options

There is a wide range of options available where you can live. These include sheltered environments through to ordinary housing. Most importantly, the option you choose should always meet your individual needs. The choices can include:

- residential communities in town and rural locations
- group homes
- hostels
- home ownership with support
- council/housing association rental with support
- therapeutic communities
- further education/residential colleges
- parental home with support
- outreach support
- respite care.

Who provides the housing?

Local authorities and health authorities are no longer the main provider of residential care, particularly since the National Health and Community Care Act of 1990. The local authority now has the responsibility to 'enable' people with autism to access services provided by others.

Finding out about housing services available in your area

The following organisations and people may be able to give you information about the housing services available in your area:

- social services
- health authorities
- GPs
- Council for Voluntary Services (CVS)
- voluntary organisations
- national organisations
- local support groups
- friends/colleagues.

Find details of these people and organisations in your local phonebook.

What are your rights?

- As a disabled person you have the rights under current law to an assessment   (see next section) with a six months time limit from application to completion.
  NB It is this assessment which is the gateway to any housing service for you.
- You are entitled to know precisely what decision has been reached and why.
- A service cannot be taken away or reduced unless another assessment has proven that you, or your carer's, needs have changed.
- You can be charged for services.
- If you are not satisfied then you have the right to complain, firstly using social services complaints procedure. If you are still unhappy with the outcome of any assessment or provision of service, use the following routes:
  - the local authority
  - your local MP
  - the ombudsman
  - the secretary of state.

NB Always lodge your grievances in a structured thoughtful way.

- Use the law if you need to. If you are on income support you will automatically receive free legal aid.
- Remember! The local authority is there to provide a service for you.

The first steps!

- Register with the local authority housing department as being in need of accommodation.
- Make a referral to your local social services department for a Community Care Assessment (CCA).

The social services department will have a duty to assess your needs usually as long as you are a resident in the area of the local authority.

Since the Community Care Act, assessment and care management are the gateway to any package of housing service for people with autism and Asperger syndrome.

A social services department should accept the initial referral and may request support from:

- yourself
- your parents, carers or guardian
- a friend
- a representative of a voluntary organisation (advocates)
- your GP or other professionals (social worker)
- any other person acting on behalf of you.

The assessment

Different local authorities have different assessment procedures. The assessment procedure may be a simple assessment or a comprehensive multi disciplinary assessment which operates on many levels (for a housing application the latter is more likely).

A care manager (CM) will be appointed who will be given the responsibility for making the assessment. The care manager should get to know you and talk with the following people:

- the person being assessed (you)
- parent/carer
- day centre staff
- GP
- Social Services and health staff
- others.

What information should be included in an assessment?

Under the Chronically Sick and Disabled Persons Act 1970 (Section 2) the following services must be provided to a disabled person once the need for those services has been identified in an assessment.

- Practical assistance in the home
- Radio, library, TV or similar recreational facilities
- Lectures, games, outings or other recreational facilities outside the home
- Assistance for an individual to take advantage of educational facilities
- Travel to and from home for an individual to participate in services
- Carrying out works of adaptation to the home
- Provision of facilities for the individual's greater safety, comfort or convenience
- To take holidays, whether provided by the Local Authority or another organisation
- Meals for an individual at home or elsewhere
- Provision of a telephone and any special equipment so that an individual can use the telephone.

In order to get the best assessment you or your parent/carer need to also consider the following issues:

- Personal care - what type of support do you need? How many hours do you need it and when do you need if for?
- Housing needs

- Equipment - complete radio or TV equipment for example
- Independent living skills
- Shopping
- Social skills
- Employment/further education assistance to take advantage of these facilities.

If is important that before an assessment you:
- find out lots of information
- write down what you want to say and be clear about what you want to happen
- choose where to meet, what day/time suits you
- ask for a copy of the criteria they are going to use in the assessment.

During the assessment it is most important to remember that it is your assessment:
- don't be intimidated
- speak for as long as you need to
- use notes
- ask questions
- check what has been written down
- ask for a copy of the assessment
- take an advocate with you. (see Chapter 11 for more information about advocacy.)

What happens next?

After the assessment has taken place, a care plan will be drawn up. This will outline, what support you need, where you might be able to get it, and how much it will cost.

The care manager will be responsible for trying to get the services you need.

Who chooses where you live?

The care manager who carried out the assessment will show you a list of homes/options and probably tell you the maximum amount of money that social services will give you. You can choose from those options.

Funding

The care plan will consider the resources available that best meet your requirements. Local authorities are facing budget cuts year after year and this can result in tighter eligibility criteria, higher charges to residents, lower cost package of care and even home closures!

This is a particularly complex area and things are changing all the time! The best option for you is to get expert advice at the time through a Citizen's Advice Bureau (CAB), Welfare Rights Centre or specialist voluntary organisations such as the NAS.

Buying the property

- You or your family can purchase a house yourselves.
- The property could be owned by an independent private or voluntary organisation.
- It might be a local authority owned specialist residential service property.
- It might be a council owned property for renting.
- The property could be purchased by and managed by a local housing association.

The running costs

The running costs can be met by any of the following:
- a payment by the local authority for an individual or a group of people in a home [1]
- a contribution by you after a financial assessment
- housing benefit (claimed by you)
- The Independent Living Fund (claimed by you)
- other benefits (Income Support, DLA Mobility Allowance etc claimed by you)
- Special Needs Management Allowance (SNMA) (claimed by Housing Association if their property).

---

[1] People with a disability (including autism) may receive money to purchase their own services in the future.

Conclusion

Each one of you will have different needs and wishes with regards to where you want to live after leaving home. The rest of your family, particularly your parents, will also have needs and strong views about the type of support housing they think you require.

- Be clear about what housing needs you have and be confident about speaking up and making those needs known.
- Be informed and be informed early. Collect information, make contact with all the relevant people at an early stage and develop a good understanding of how the system works in your area. If you don't know, know a man/woman who does!

The relevant acts and legislation

The National Health and Community Care Act 1990

The Chronically Sick and Disabled Person's Act

The Registered Homes Act 1984

Portfield School

4 Madgeleine Lane
Christchurch
Dorset
BH23 1PH

Tel: 01202 486626
Fax: 01202 483677
E-mail portfield@lds.co.uk

Portfield school is a day and weekly residential school for children with autism aged 2-19. The main aims of our school education are to help the children overcome and cope with the triad of impariments, and to maximise their opportunities for independent living.

The school:

- has recently enjoyed favourable OFSTED and social services inspections.

- is committed to high quality training for all of its staff.

- employs its own specialist speech and language therapist, music therapist and educational psychologist.

- has successfuly gained planning premission to build new purpose build premises in order to expand provision for 63 pupils

- is committed to the use of non-aversive and positve methods of behavioural intervention.

- is involved in many succesful integration projects and liaises closely with local mainstream schools

- is registered and fully accredited as part of the National Autistic Society quality audit and accrediation programme.

If you would like further details please contact Peter Gabony, the Head teacher, in order to receive our brochure or arrange a visit.

Chapter 11

Advocacy and how it can help you

Jan Snook, NAS Development Manager for the South West and Mid-Counties Region

Many people with autistic spectrum disorders have difficulty in understanding relationships, getting on with people, making choices and sometimes not wanting to do anything. We all have to make choices and decisions every day and this can be very stressful for everyone including people with autistic spectrum disorders.

Even if we do know what we want, being able to explain this can also be extremely difficult. To have someone who understands what you want and who can help you to tell other people can be very useful. This person is called an advocate.

What is advocacy?

Advocacy means to plead for or speak on behalf of another person. Parents have often been their son/daughter's advocate. Sometimes they are helped by social workers or voluntary agencies to speak on behalf of their son/daughter on issues such as diagnosis, education, day care, adult services, employment and residential services.

What is self advocacy?

Self advocacy means people being their own advocates and speaking for themselves, so that your life goes the way you want it to. These concepts are summarised in the CMH manual (CMH/LASAI 1988):

'Speaking up means telling other people what you think, how you feel and what matters to you.

'Everyone should speak up:
- when they think something is important
- when they want something to happen
- when they want something to stop happening
- when decisions are being made about their life.

'Your family, friends and other people who work around you will not know your point of view unless you speak up and tell them.

'No one can read your mind!!' [1]

To be able to have a voice, to be heard and listened to, the following skills need to be developed:
- **Communication skills** – talking and listening to other people
- **Social skills** – to know what to do and how to behave in situations with other people
- **Ability to make decisions**
- **Self confidence** – to state what you would like to do or achieve and to learn any new skills that will help to do this.

Some of these skills may be very difficult to learn and you will need the help and support of any professionals working with you, your family and friends.

You also need to learn to cope with the frustration and disappointment when you do not get what you want and again you will need support with this.

Self·advocacy does not mean that every adult with an autistic spectrum disorder can, or should, make major decisions independently. Few people do. Family, and friends may all play a part in helping you to make choices which fit in with your own wishes (McFaggart and Gould, 1988).

---

[1] VIA (Values Into Action), formally CMH, Oxford House, Derbyshire Street, London E2 6HG

How advocacy helped – an example

A young man with Asperger syndrome, William, describes how an advocate helped him to develop a social life. William did not have the confidence to go out on his own; he did not know what to say to people or recognise when he had upset them. William hoped that the advocate could help him regain his confidence and make new friends. Before his advocate could help him, William had to educate him on Asperger syndrome. They also had to get to know each other as individuals. William says that the key to successful advocacy is good communication. For you, as a person with Asperger syndrome, communication can be quite difficult at times. This means that your advocate needs to take the lead role in keeping the lines of communication open.

Some tips from William
• Advocates should not 'assume' that a person with autistic spectrum disorder always understands.
• When promises are broken, even for a very good reason, it is extremely upsetting for the person with an autistic spectrum disorder.
• Most importantly, advocates shouldn't just focus on the autism. As William says, 'that is not everything I am'.

Advocates can help in many different ways. Other examples might be finding somewhere to live, looking at job opportunities and DSS benefits or an appointment with a professional.

How to find an advocate

Unfortunately, it's not always easy to find an advocate who is knowledgeable about autistic spectrum disorders. However, there are people and organisations to help you with this.

The Autism Helpline
393 City Road
London
EC1V 1NG
Tel 0171 903 3555 (lines are open 10-11.30 am and 2-3.30 pm weekdays)

The NAS Autism Helpline may be able to give you information on organisations across the UK and put you in contact with people who are advocates in your local area.

The Citizen Advocacy, Information and Training
164 Lee Valley Techno Park
Ashley Road
London
N17 9LN
Tel 0181 880 4545

This organisation should have a list of regional contacts for you.

Local contacts

Locally you could try the following organisations:

- Citizens advocacy schemes
- Citizens advice bureau
- Volunteer bureau
- Community voluntary service
- Social services departments – your social worker
- Local autistic societies
- Befriending schemes often run by voluntary agencies, eg Mencap.

Gloucestershire Group Homes

Small group homes in the community providing support and training for adults with diagnosis of Asperger syndrome

Spring Mill Business Centre
Avening Road, Nailsworth, Glos GL6 0BS
Tel: 01453 835023   Fax: 01453 836932

Gloucestershire Group Homes was established as an independent voluntary organisation with charitable status in March 1994. Previously, two of our five homes were incorporated in an organisation that was originally set up by parents of children with the diagnosis of autism in the 1980s.

During the past 3 years Gloucestershire Group Homes has developed its service and has focused on providing an appropriate environment and support system for those individuals with the diagnosis of high functioning Autism/Asperger Syndrome.

The main aim of Gloucestershire Group Homes is to provide a safe and caring environment that enables people to achieve their fullest potential, taking into account the individual's intellectual, physical, emotional and social abilities.

Supporting people to achieve as much independence in their lives as possible is a priority of Gloucestershire Group Homes.

Gloucestershire Group Homes do not hold a "waiting list", although we do take referrals and will contact individual requests if and when a vacancy arises. Each individual will be assessed and costed depending on needs.

For further information, please contact the manager at the above address.

Chapter 12

Finding work

Russell Harding, Employment Support Worker at
Prospects, the NAS supported employment service

Introduction

Some of you may be aware of the work that Prospects is doing in London to
support people with Asperger syndrome[1] in their search to obtain work.
Many people who have obtained positions, have gone on to become valued
employees working in a range of different areas. Examples of people
currently registered with Prospects and working, include computer
programmers, administrators, laboratory technicians and warehouse staff.

At the moment Prospects only covers the London area, although we hope to
expand to other areas of the country in the future. This short article is
intended to be useful for those people with Asperger syndrome looking for
work outside the London area. It gives general information about how to get
advice and support locally as well as advice in looking for work.

Choosing the right career

Choosing what kind of work to do can be difficult for lots of people.
Sometimes you can know what kind of things you are good at and what you
enjoy, but it can be more difficult to decide how this could lead to the right

---

[1] This article may also be relevant to those of you who are able but have a diagnosis of autism.

job. When thinking about the jobs you want to pursue it is important to **always select a type of work that is going to match your particular strengths and talents**. This may sound obvious but it is extremely important to bear in mind.

Although of course people with Asperger syndrome are all very different, there are some useful guidelines to follow when thinking about your career. Prospects has clients who have followed these particular guidelines and have, in most cases, gone on to choose a job that they can be successful in.

Avoid jobs that require advanced people, or interaction, skills

These include most jobs that involve serving customers, selling things or acting as a representative for an organisation, eg receptionist work.

Choosing a job that does not involve high interaction skills does not mean that you won't meet people at work. You will find that there will be plenty of time to meet and talk with the people who are your colleagues. What it does mean 'though, is that your suitability for a particular job won't be measured by your people skills.

Try to think about jobs where your work will be guided by systems, procedures or processes

If you pick a job where instructions are clear and systematic, you are likely to learn faster than a job where you are expected to organise and learn your work through 'initiative'.

If you find change or surprises difficult, try to identify work that has an element of structure or routine to it

Many jobs fit this category and still have some variety to them. Often however this variety is planned or can be predicted. Always remember that although you like things to be predictable, many people who do not have Asperger syndrome do not like too much routine. The fact that you prefer more routine work may be seen as an asset by an employer.

You may find that you are not sure what kind of jobs are available or that you are not sure what you are capable of. Write a list of things that you are good at or enjoy. If you haven't worked before, think about what you were good at, at school or what you are good at in your general day to day life activities. For example, it may be that you are good at planning where you are supposed to be and what you are supposed to be doing. If so, you may be someone with good organisational skills. Here are a few examples of the kind of things that you might include in a list of skills if they apply to you. If there are ones that are not included on the list below, write them down anyway as the list below is only an example.

Example list of strengths
- Particular qualifications that you have.
- Particular experience you have of a job or that you have gained in voluntary work.
- Good memory (perhaps you are someone who can remember the detailed facts about an event that happened a long time ago, or you may know a large number of facts about a particular topic).
- Good organisation (eg, if you plan your life in detail).
- Reliability (you may rarely be late for an appointment. If so, then this may apply to you).
- Good with figures (even if you don't have a qualification, do you find that you can use arithmetic easily in your day to day life – for instance calculating your 'change' in a shop instantly).
- Good concentration (some people with Asperger syndrome can concentrate on tasks that other people find repetitive and boring and still have a high level of concentration).
- Artistic or a creative ability (again, even if you don't have a qualification, have you got a hobby that involves something creative – this may be a relevant skill for work).
- Being able to work without disturbing others (if you are a 'quiet' person, this may be a quality valued by employers as you are more likely to get on with your work and not disturb other people).

It may be useful to get advice from family and trusted friends about what they think you are good at. Compare this to your list and if you think they have relevant points then add them to your list. Don't worry if you find making a list of skills difficult, it is unlikely to mean that you don't have skills, just that you don't yet know them or that you find identifying them difficult!

The careers service

Another good source of advice can be from the careers service (sometimes also called 'Lifetime Careers'). They can give you **general** information about different types of jobs and can tell you how to find out about applying for them. They often have useful lists of organisations to contact if you are looking for a job in a particular area. They don't give detailed advice on things like filling out applications or interview techniques. Advice on this can be found from other organisations who are listed in this article.

In most areas their telephone number will be listed with directory enquiries or within the phone book. If you can't find the number, your local borough council or your nearest college of further education (which will be in the phone book) should be able to give the number to you.

Always ring the careers service beforehand to find out when a good time to make an appointment would be. Also, check beforehand what people they work with to make sure that you fit into that category. For example, sometimes they will be a careers service for under 19 year olds or perhaps for graduates only, or they may give careers advice to all people.

After all this you still may be unsure what job you want to do. If this happens, **don't worry!** Lots of people in life generally, who have been working for some time still can be unsure whether the career they are in is right for them. They often just don't admit to it! You may be someone who perhaps needs to 'test out' a particular job before you decide whether you like it. If this is the case this can sometimes be possible – how to do this and where to go is explained in more detail below.

Types of support/help you might find useful

As people with Asperger syndrome are all different, the kind of assistance you are likely to need may well be very different from someone else who is reading this article. Before making contact with organisations who can provide support it is extremely useful to think about and plan what help you think that you might need.

Discussing this with family or friends may also help and it may be a good idea to write it down for future reference. If you do this it will mean that when you meet with organisations you are more likely to get the advice and assistance that you need as you will be able to tell them about it.

Think about what might be useful:
- to help you find a job
- to do that job well.

Are there things that you know in the past you have found difficult? Are there things about working and/or applying for work that you know you could learn about given the chance, but that you haven't had the opportunity to?

Because everyone is different some people might benefit from a lot of support on a large range of things while others may only require a small amount of advice in a particular area.

On the next page is a checklist that might help you think about what advice would be useful. You could go down each point and think whether advice on this would be useful for you. It's a good idea to write down the kind of support you would like. For example, it may be that you find it difficult to understand what interviewers are asking you, whereas someone else may find that they can answer questions in an interview but find making eye contact almost impossible.

Getting advice and support

There may be a number of organisations in your area that can help and advise you on finding work. The number and type of organisations will vary according to where you live. For example, in large cities there are often a range of organisations who can help, whereas there may be less if you live in a more rural area.

Your employment service – Job Centre
The first thing to do to get some advice and support is to contact your local employment service – Job Centre. There is likely to be one of these in your

Checklists

This is not intended to be a complete list. If you have other ideas, then include these as well if you think that help on that area would be useful.

Getting work

❑ Knowing what kind of job suits you
❑ Knowing where to find out about vacancies
❑ Filling out application forms
❑ Designing and sending CVs to companies
❑ Being successful at interviews
❑ Whether and when to tell your employer about Asperger syndrome

At work

❑ Understanding instructions
❑ Organising your work efficiently
❑ Dealing with change
❑ Getting on with colleagues
❑ Coping with stress or anxiety
❑ Whether and when to tell colleagues about Asperger syndrome

area whether you live in a city or not. The person you will need to contact will be the **Disability Employment Advisor** (DEA) who will work at the job centre. The telephone number can be found in the telephone book and it is always better for a first meeting to ring to make an appointment rather than just 'turning up' without phoning first. You need to explain to them that you have a disability, that you are looking for work and that you would like to arrange a time to come in and meet them to discuss how they can help.

The DEA's job is to provide advice and assistance to people with disabilities who want to look for work or who would like to get some experience of working. Because they work with people with a range of disabilities the amount that they know about Asperger syndrome will vary. It is always useful to take a small leaflet about Asperger syndrome with you to the first meeting with the DEA in case they would like more information. These leaflets can be sent to you if you telephone the NAS Autism Helpline on **0171 903 3555** and request them.

Important: Always ask the DEA whether they would like some more information about Asperger syndrome before giving them the leaflet. If you do not do this it may inadvertently seem to them that you are questioning their ability to do the job, especially if they do know about Asperger syndrome already.

Checklists

Checklist of things to take with you when you meet the DEA

- A leaflet about Asperger syndrome (but ask them first if they want more information).
- Your CV if you have one.
- Notes you have made about what support you think you may need.
- Notes you have made about what your strengths are.

Other things that it is useful to take to first meetings with a DEA, include your CV (if you have one already, don't worry if you don't) the notes that you may have made about what support you think that you might need and the notes that you have made about your strengths. These things can often be useful but are not always necessary for a first meeting. Don't worry if they are not asked for, they are useful to take anyway.

For some people who have Asperger syndrome their disability is very 'hidden'. It is not obvious to people who meet them for the first time, what difficulties they might have. If you think that this applies to you (you could always ask a friend if you are unsure) then you should make sure that you definitely tell the DEA about the difficulties that you have to prevent them from thinking that you don't need any assistance.

For other people with Asperger syndrome their disability may be more obvious to people when they meet them for the first time. Sometimes, people can incorrectly assume that a person with Asperger syndrome is not as intelligent as they really are. This can be the case if the person is particularly quiet or has difficulty in saying what they mean. If you think this applies to you then you should make sure that you tell the DEA about the strengths that you have so that the intelligence that you have will be obvious in the meeting.

Other services that may be available

Job coaches/support workers
There may be an organisation in your area that can provide job coaches / support workers (they are often called different things but do the same job) when you start a job or a work experience placement. Job coaches are people who can come with you to work and help in a variety of areas. Job coaches can make sure that instructions are given clearly and give you extra training if this is necessary. They can also give advice about how to make good relationships with colleagues or perhaps help you to cope effectively with anxiety or with changes at work. They can also explain about Asperger syndrome to managers.

Training courses to help you find work
DEAs can also sometimes arrange for you to go on courses that provide training on how to find a job. These courses train you to develop skills for interviews, fill in application forms more effectively, design good CVs and organise an efficient and effective job search. These courses are often combined with more practical work skills training, such as developing IT and computer skills. They are usually shorter courses than conventional college courses and often last for between 10 to 16 weeks. Attendance may be either full time or part time but is often flexible.

Training courses to develop specific work-related skills
DEAs can also arrange for you to go on courses to train for a particular skill. Often these courses lead to a recognised qualification, such as NVQ or GNVQ. There are a wide range of courses available covering lots of different areas. Your DEA will be able to give you information on what is available.

Work experience

If you would like to 'test out' a particular job or if you would like to develop more experience but do not feel a paid job would be the best option, then DEAs can also arrange for a period of 'work experience'. Work experience is usually around six weeks long and although unpaid (travel expenses and lunch are currently paid) is often very useful.

PACT assessments

DEAs can arrange for you to have a PACT assessment, which is a series of tests, designed to find out what skills you have and what jobs you are likely to be good at. Generally, the tests last for a morning and are practically based, eg testing sorting ability or IT skills. It is often useful to have an assessment if you are not sure of what you are capable of and you may even find a particular skill or strength that you did not know you had!

Although the DEA can tell you what organisations are available in your area, you may want to find this information out for yourself and contact these organisations directly. **The Association For Supported Employment** keeps a list of organisations operating in England. Their details are:

The Association for Supported Employment
Pennine View
Gamblesby
Penrith,
CA10 1HR

Tel/Fax: 01768 881225
E mail: afse@Onyxnet.co.uk.

Telling employers about Asperger syndrome

Telling people about your disability may be difficult. This is definitely the case when deciding whether to tell an employer or a potential employer about your disability. It is Prospects' experience that in most cases it is to people's advantage to tell an employer about their Asperger syndrome and to give some information about what Asperger syndrome is.

If you are already in a job you may want to tell your employer about your disability. Doing this may mean that they are then able to make changes to your role that make your life easier and/or make you a more effective employee. Before doing this, get advice on the best way to explain things. Your DEA or possibly someone from a local NAS Branch may be able to help.

Why tell an employer about Asperger syndrome?

There are a number of reasons why it is often useful to tell an employer about your disability. The main reason is because in the long run it means you are likely to be more successful at work and probably will find work less stressful. If people are aware that you need things explained to you clearly and logically then you will find that people give you better instructions and actually make what they mean a lot more obvious. If they don't know anything about Asperger syndrome then they can hardly be blamed for explaining things badly!

You are also likely to find that in the longer term you will be able to establish better relations with your colleagues if they know about Asperger syndrome. Colleagues are likely to be more tolerant. For some people with Asperger syndrome, making minor social 'faux pas' does not happen very often. If it does happen and colleagues do not know it is connected with Asperger syndrome, they may incorrectly assume that the person is being rude or unthoughtful. If they know about the disability then they are less likely to think this.

The final reason why it is often better to tell an employer about your Asperger syndrome is connected with the Disability Discrimination Act (DDA). This Act requires 'large' employers to look into making a 'reasonable adaptation' to a job if it would allow someone with a disability to take up or remain in that position. If an employer does not know about your disability then they have much less of an obligation to adapt a job. So telling your employer can lead to changes in your job which are beneficial both for you and your employer.

It is important to remember that it is generally not very effective to go raising the topic of the law. There is a big risk that if you do this you may come across as pushy and/or militant. Sometimes, it may be relevant to talk to your employer about the DDA, but if you think that this is the case it will generally be more effective to get the help of someone else who deals regularly with employers on this issue (eg DEAs or some job coaches may be able to do this on your behalf). In most cases they will then be 'diplomatic' with the employer by discussing an adaptation first. Then, if it is necessary and helpful, they may talk about the DDA.

Telling potential employers about Asperger syndrome

It can also be useful to tell potential employers about Asperger syndrome so that they are able to adapt the interview slightly to give you a fairer chance. The best time to do this is either when you fill out your application form or if you are called to the actual interview. On some application forms there is a section asking whether you have any specific requirements at interview. You can use this section to include the advice that is listed below. Some applications forms will have a 'Two Ticks' symbol on them which looks like this:

If this is on the form, this means that any applicant for the job who meets the minimum skills and experience criteria and who also has a disability is guaranteed an interview for the position. This is sometimes also called the guaranteed interview scheme.

If there is no section about disabilities on the application form then it is best to contact the employer before the interview, or get someone to do it on your behalf (eg DEA). If you explain the following practical points to the employer before hand this will give you a much better chance at interview.

- (If this applies to you) Explain that you may have difficulty with eye contact and that this is part of your Asperger syndrome. Some interviewers rate interview candidates on their eye contact. If you tell them in advance, they should avoid rating you unfairly on this.
- Explain that you are a very logical person and that you may find 'open', (ie vague, questions) confusing. Explain that if you are given specific, clear questions you will be able to respond much more effectively. Say that you are much better answering questions when the answers are factual but that because of Asperger syndrome you will find 'hypothetical' or 'general' questions difficult.
- If asked what your disability is, explain that it is a **mild** form of autism (stress the 'mild' part) and that it does not affect your intelligence.
- Always stress your positive qualities in any conversation about your Asperger syndrome. For example, you might be really thorough in your work, very reliable or have a good technical ability or particular skill.

Some people have in the past argued that it is better to 'lie' or cover up the fact that you have a disability. Prospects acknowledges that this may well be an opinion that has resulted from bad experiences with employers in the past, but in general does not agree that this approach would help you get a job. If an employer was going to discriminate and not call someone for an interview because of their disability, then they are unlikely to be a good employer to work for anyway and you would be better off applying elsewhere.

Employers are now increasingly more positive and recognise that because of the skills and abilities that many people with disabilities have it makes good business sense to give people a fair chance in the recruitment process.

THE SPRINGS COMMUNITY
Coast Drive, St Mary's Bay,
Romney Marsh, Kent, TN29 0HN
Telephone: 01797 363550

The Springs Community is a spacious residential home on the Kent Coast offering high quality specialist services to adults affected by autism and Asperger's Syndrome. The main building accommodates twelve residents in single en-suite rooms. From summer 1999, a terrace of four 'semi-independent' houses will be available in the grounds. Facilities include:-

- large television lounge: quiet lounge; fully-equipped training kitchen; private room with entertaining facilities for residents' visitors; minibuses and cars available for residents' use; menus to suit individual preferences and specialised diets

- excellent sporting and recreational facilities including fully-equipped gymnasium, full sized outdoor heated swimming pool, tennis court and squash court

- qualified and caring staff - available day and night - who support residents' individual development programmes

- large gardens with private access to beach and safe walking and cycling areas along the sea wall; shopping facilities, cafes, restaurants, community agencies etc. within walking distance; frequent bus services to surrounding towns.

For an information pack or more information
please contact the manager
Registered in the Autism Services Accreditation Programme

Chapter 13

Socialising – anecdotes of social life

Thomas Madar, Software Developer at Boots, Prospects' client and person with Asperger syndrome

Scarcely does a bigger problem exist for a person with Asperger syndrome than that of attracting popularity and friendship from the community which surround him. For many, an ascent of the Matterhorn with bare feet would be a more achievable option. Why is this?

A number of reasons come to mind. In my case, major difficulties in the following areas have been instrumental in attracting irritation and rejection from others:
* picking up implicit rules of conduct ranging from conformity to changes in fashion to social graces
* looking people in the eye
* interpreting and giving non-verbal signals in the use of the hands, intonation of voice etc
* being aware of what people will think of me before acting in a particular way
* control of moods and emotions, leading to visible mood and temperament changes
* generation of small talk and continuous spontaneous conversation.

However, the following compensations have spared me from the state of total rejection:
* a keen Christian faith, and an adherence to the values entertained by the Bible. This has also been instrumental in determining my social universe
* perseverance

- attention to quality
- a keen memory for facts and figures.

The following paragraphs describe my adventures in a variety of common social situations. They describe the steps which I took to gain social acceptance and to make friends from early adulthood in the mid-1970s to the present day.

School days

School days provide the earliest opportunity for social contact for the vast majority of people, and yet, I remember these days with trepidation. In my primary school days, I was teased a lot, but did manage to make one or two close friends, and got invited to the occasional birthday party. I remember my early birthday parties being well attended by my classmates.

My journey through secondary school was very rough. Looking back, I can clearly see what caused all this teasing and hostility:

- I used to run everywhere around the school and in a most peculiar fashion. Other people walked.
- I stared into space, talked to myself, and laughed at my own private jokes on countless occasions within ear and eye shot of other pupils.
- I had visible mood swings, and frequently shouted out loud for no apparent reason.
- I refused to conform to the dictates of fashion, continuing to dress in an outmoded way and retaining a liking for classical music long after my peers started embracing pop.
- I was afraid to stick up for myself when bullied, thereby encouraging more bullying.
- I could be very obnoxious at times, bragging about my academic successes when others found academic work very difficult.

If only I had had the right sort of professional support at school while on the school premises, life would have been so much easier! Someone to make me less oblivious of the impression which I was giving to other pupils, and to give me strategies to defend myself when bullied would have been so useful.

At work

In the work environment, relationships with team colleagues and the supervisor/manager are of crucial importance. In my first job after having graduated from university, I had real difficulty fitting in, which contributed to me being made redundant in 1980. In subsequent work situations, my relations with others in the office varied with the suitability of the work which I was assigned.

I illustrate this with an example. In the mid-1980s, I was working as a software engineer for Marconi Radar in Chelmsford, and was given the role of a designer/team leader on a project involving the production of a military air traffic control system. Lacking the interpersonal skills required for effective team leadership, I had real difficulty in being accepted by my team, and by others working with me. I was also addressed and treated like a child by my supervisor, and later given a bad appraisal.

A few months later, I was assigned a much more suitable role as that of a project support programmer, and had a superb conversational relationship with both my colleagues and my supervisor.

Relationships at home

Almost as important as relationships at work, are relationships at home, when sharing accommodation with a landlord, landlady or other tenants. For me, such relationships have always worked out, even when the circumstances were somewhat trying.

In the opening months of 1990, I took lodgings with a very difficult landlord who treated his lodgers like children. Among other things, he forbade us to invite our friends into the house, to use the house phone for outgoing calls and allowed us to use the bathroom for baths only at certain times of the week. And yet, against all odds, I got on well with him. And to such a degree that we sent each other Christmas cards for a number of years after I had moved out.

Social relationships

After school, over time, I have lost almost all of my idiosyncrasies and have found it progressively easier to become accepted into the community. Nowhere was I more successful in gaining acceptance and friendship than within the environs of my local church, or any organisation connected with the Christian faith.

The vast majority of my friends have been made as a result of attending various local churches in my movements around the country. When I was studying for an MPhil in Software Engineering during the late 1980s, the Elim Pentecostal Church at Aberystwyth stood out as being particularly welcoming. During the course of 15 months, I managed to make at least four friends, inviting, and being invited for meals.

Outside of church, I was welcome at University Christian Unions, and whatever Christian Fellowship there was at work. I made a number of excellent friends from these fellowships. During my MPhil course, I remember one of them being a keen rambler and we frequently took the bus into the outlying regions of mid Wales for a day's hiking.

My social relationships with people in areas outside Christianity, work and home varied from spectacular failure to a moderate degree of success. On the whole, I was somewhat discouraged, and have only very recently started reaching out again.

I have enjoyed memberships of a multitude of clubs and societies, both inside and outside university, which worked out well. Particularly good examples of these are the Youth Hostels Association (1979), Roteract Club of Chelmsford (mid-1980s), The Open University Students' Association (mid-1980s) and University of Wales' Railway and Transport Association (1987).

Practices that have helped me in social relationships

Over the years, the following practices have helped me in social relationships, especially at work:

Pro-active conversation

The practice of being the first to greet a person, asking them how their weekend or holiday went and asking questions about themselves has been much better in attracting conversation and friendship than merely answering other people's questions. On numerous occasions, such pro-activity has meant the difference between my partner leaving me after a few introductory words and a long conversation.

Appropriate non-verbal signals

When conversing, or attending meetings, the following have conveyed a good impression and attracted the right kind of interest:

• looking the speaker in the eye
• not fidgeting, yawning or dozing off, looking around, or showing other signs of inattention or boredom

Feedback

When given any sort of instruction, I have found it essential to re-iterate this back to the instructor in my own words to convey the impression that I have paid attention and that I understand what I have to do.

Appropriate levels of detail

When someone asks me about something to open a social conversation, for example 'did you have a good holiday?', I have found it appropriate to answer in summary, only going into detail if further information is requested. Plunging immediately into detail is likely to irritate my partner if he or she is in a hurry.

Other people conversing

When a conversation is in progress, I have found it appropriate to stay away unless a contribution can by made to the subject of the conversation. Unpleasant consequences have frequently followed any attempt to interrupt. These have varied from my questions being answered, then the conversation continuing as though I no longer existed, to the words 'excuse us, we are talking' being said to me in the tone usually reserved for naughty children.

Conclusion

To sum up, this essay has dealt with my social life at school, at work, at home, in connection with religion and in other areas. I had a hard time at school, but from my university days onwards, my social situation became easier. I feel that the quality of my life would have been substantially improved had I had on-site social skills coaching and support, particularly at school and in some work situations.

The fact remains that adequate interpersonal skills are crucial for successful independent living, for it is by these that society judges us for much of our worth. We require such skills to defend ourselves, to persuade/control/lead others, to make friends, to be successful in job interviews, to be promoted to positions of responsibility in organisations, to create and keep a marriage together, and to bring up children. To be without means to be profoundly vulnerable and disadvantaged, and this is the situation faced by the vast majority of people with an autistic spectrum condition.

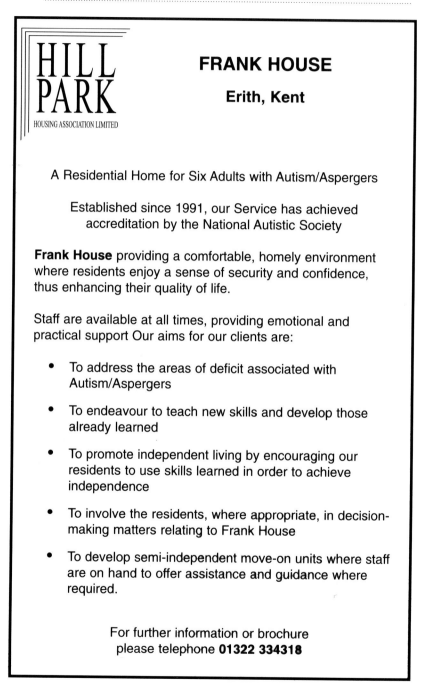

HILL PARK
HOUSING ASSOCIATION LIMITED

FRANK HOUSE
Erith, Kent

A Residential Home for Six Adults with Autism/Aspergers

Established since 1991, our Service has achieved accreditation by the National Autistic Society

Frank House providing a comfortable, homely environment where residents enjoy a sense of security and confidence, thus enhancing their quality of life.

Staff are available at all times, providing emotional and practical support Our aims for our clients are:

- To address the areas of deficit associated with Autism/Aspergers

- To endeavour to teach new skills and develop those already learned

- To promote independent living by encouraging our residents to use skills learned in order to achieve independence

- To involve the residents, where appropriate, in decision-making matters relating to Frank House

- To develop semi-independent move-on units where staff are on hand to offer assistance and guidance where required.

For further information or brochure
please telephone **01322 334318**

Chapter 14

Resources

*Items available from the Publications Department have a (P) listed after
the title or if they are available from the Information Centre you will find a
(I) listed after the title. To obtain copies, please refer to the Publications
List (Section VI of this Handbook) or for articles available from the
Information Centre please write to the Information Centre at The National
Autistic Society, 393 City Road, London EC1V 1NG. Please note that book
prices are correct at the time of print but these may be subject to change.*

Asperger United (P)
This is a quarterly newsletter, edited by a person with Asperger syndrome.
It contains articles either written by people with Asperger syndrome or by
professionals with this group specifically in mind. There are four issues
each year. Subscription £4 UK, £6 overseas.

Grandin, T (1986) *Emergence labelled autistic.* Warner Books £9.99 plus
p&p (P)
One of the first books ever written by a person with autism, the book gives
the reader a fascinating and unique insight into the nature of autism.

Grandin, T (1996) *Thinking in pictures.* Vintage Books £9.99 plus p&p
(P)
The author offers her insights into autism and the way people with autism
think and act.

Howlin, P (1996) *Autism: preparing for adulthood* Routledge £14.99 plus
p&p (P)
The author focuses on adults with autism and their families. By using
information from research studies and treatment programmes, it provides a
practical resource for parents, carers and autistic people themselves. The
author discusses problems and solutions related to educational and
occupational attainments and ways of coping with psychiatric and other
difficulties and fostering independence in later life.

Segar, M (1997) *A guide to coping specifically for people with Asperger
syndrome.* The Early Years Centre
The publication is designed to make you aware of the many unwritten rules
which most people instinctively know and take for granted. A lot of the
material included was written on the basis of Marc's own personal
experiences and includes information about: body language, holding a
conversation, humour, sexually related problems and points about going
out and also making friends, living aware from home, jobs and interviews,
driving and travelling abroad.
The Early Years Centre, Sutherland House, 272 Longdale Lane,
Ravenshead, Nottinghamshire NG15 9AH

Williams, D (1994) *Nobody Nowhere* Transworld Publishers £6.99 plus
p&p (P)
A moving account of Donna's struggle to come to terms with her life with
autism and to survive the suffering of an unsympathetic and ignorant
world.

Williams, D (1994) ***Somebody Somewhere*** Transworld Publishers £6.99 plus p&p (P)
The sequel to Nobody Nowhere which explores the four years since diagnosis and her attempts to leave her 'world under glass' and live 'normally'.

Williams, D (1996) ***Like colour to the blind*** Times books £15.99 plus p&p (P)
Offers an intimate diary of joys and stresses of falling in love as she continues her struggle with autism.

The Kent Autistic Trust

14 High Street, Brompton,
Gillingham, Kent, ME7 5AE.
Tel: 01834 405168   Fax: 01634 811282

The Kent Autistic Trust is a registered charity, a non-profit making organisation that is a company limited by guarantee. It is affiliated to the National Autistic Society (NAS).

The Trust was started in 1985 by parents to provide a specialist service to respond to the needs of people with autism and their families. Membership is open to families, friends, staff and other individuals or professionals interested in autism.

The aims of the Trust are:
• To develop specialised residential homes and day support facilities for people with autism.
• To provide support and advocacy services for people with autism and their families.
• To identify and represent all people with autism in Kent
• To define their needs and stimulate services to fulfil those needs
• To develop the individual towards increasing confidence, independence, integration and control over their own life.

The Trust offers 52 week a year residential support within small homes for up to six people. We endeavour to create a family environment with residents taking part in all aspects of the running of the home whatever their ability. All homes are Registered with the local authority and inspected on a yearly basis with the conclusions available to the public.

Our three resource centres are separately based from the residential homes to create a working atmosphere during the week day. From the resource centres people participate in a wide range of skill training, work placement and therapy.

Our future plans are:
• To continue to improve the service provided to the people with autism currently supported by the residential and day service
• To develop home and day services to meet identified need
• To build on our services to families
• To work towards extending our range of services to encompass a wider spectrum of support needs.

Contact Name: Kay Brunning, General Manager

SECTION V

For professionals

Chapter 15

Recognising autism

Dr Judith Gould, consultant clinical psychologist and Director of the NAS Centre for Social and Communication Disorders

What is the autistic spectrum?

An autistic spectrum disorder is a complex developmental disability that affects the way a person communicates and relates to people around them. The autistic spectrum includes the syndromes described by Kanner and by Asperger but is wider than these two subgroups.

Many children have a mixture of features from these two syndromes but do not fit neatly into either. The whole spectrum is defined by the presence of impairments affecting social interaction, communication and imagination, known as the triad of impairments. This is always accompanied by a narrow, repetitive range of activities.

A range of other problems is also commonly found in association with the triad but the three basic impairments are the defining criteria.

Diagnosis

Diagnosis can be difficult as there are no definitive medical diagnostic tests and the manifestations of the problems can occur at any level. Some children are very disabled with low levels of functioning. Others have superior intelligence with very high levels of skills in certain areas.

Recognising the early signs

Autism is a pattern of abnormal development that unfolds over time, so diagnosis depends upon obtaining a detailed history of the child's development and a careful assessment of skills and abilities.

- In infancy, one of the most important indications that autism could be present is the absence or very delayed development of drawing the attention of parents and others to objects or events.
- In normal childhood development, by the time children are 12 to 18 months old they are usually pointing at things and trying to engage the interest of the person they are with to invite them to look too.
- They gain attention by bringing toys and making eye contact. If this behaviour does not occur or begins very late and is limited to the child's own interests, an autistic disorder should be suspected.
- Other key signs that usually emerge in the first few years of life are the triad of impairments combined with a repetitive pattern of activities and sometimes challenging behaviour.

A triad of impairments

One of the key signs of autism is the triad of impairments, which can manifest in many ways.

Social interaction

A person with autism may:

- often appear aloof and indifferent to other people, especially other children, although some with the disorder will enjoy certain forms of active physical contact.
- passively accept social contact and even show some signs of pleasure in this but will rarely make spontaneous approaches.
- occasionally approach other people but in an odd, inappropriate, repetitive way, paying little or no attention to the responses of those they approach.

These pin people illustrate some ways in which autism is displayed

Displays
indifference

Joins in only if adult
insists and assists

One-sided
interaction

Indicates needs by
using an adult's hand

Lack of creative
pretend play

Handles or
spins objects

Echolalic - copies
words like parrot

Does not play
with other children

Talks incessantly
about one subject

Variety is not the
spice of life

No eye
contact

Bizarre
behaviour

Inappropriate
laughing
or giggling

But some can do some things very
well, very quickly but not tasks
involving social understanding

Asperger syndrome

Unlike people with 'classic' autism, who often appear withdrawn and uninterested in the world around them, many people with Asperger syndrome try hard to be sociable and do not dislike human contact. However, they still find it hard to understand non-verbal signals, including facial expressions.

Social communication

A person with autism may:

• not appreciate the social uses and pleasures of communication. This is true even of those who have a lot of speech, which they use to talk 'at' others and not 'with' them.

• not understand that language is a tool for conveying information to others. They may be able to ask for their own needs but find it hard to talk about feelings or thoughts and will not understand the emotions, ideas and beliefs of other people.

• not really understand the meaning of gestures, facial expressions or tone of voice. More able children do use gestures but these tend to be odd and inappropriate.

• understand and use language very literally, with an idiosyncratic, sometimes pompous choice of words and phrases and limited content of speech. Although some children are fascinated with words, they will not use them to interact socially.

Asperger syndrome

People with Asperger syndrome may speak very fluently but they may not take much notice of the reaction of people listening to them; they may talk on and on regardless of the listener's interest or may appear insensitive to their feelings.

Despite having good language skills, people with Asperger syndrome may sound over-precise or over-literal. Jokes can cause problems as can exaggerated language and metaphors. For example a person with Asperger syndrome may be confused or frightened by a statement like 'she bit my head off'.

Imagination

A person with autism may:

- be unable to play imaginatively with objects or toys or with other children or adults.
- tend to focus on minor or trivial things around them, for example, an earring rather than the person wearing it, or a wheel instead of the whole toy train.
- have a limited range of imaginative activities, possibly copied and pursued rigidly and repetitively.
- miss the point of pursuits involving words – eg social conversation, literature, especially fiction and subtle verbal humour.

Asperger syndrome

While they often excel at learning facts and figures, people with Asperger syndrome find it hard to think in abstract ways. This can cause problems for children in school where they may have difficulty with certain subjects, such as literature or religious studies.

Activities associated with the triad of impairments

Repetitive activities

Alongside the triad of impairments the child will always show repetitive activity or behaviour. At a simple level, this might involve repeatedly flicking their fingers or an object, such as a piece of string. More complex signs might include an insistence on following an identical route to certain places, a lengthy bedtime ritual or the repetition of a sequence of odd bodily movements.

The person can also form an intense attachment to particular objects for no apparent purpose, arrange objects in lines or patterns or collect things like pebbles or plastic bottles. They may become fascinated by certain topics, such as electricity, astronomy, birds or train timetables even specific people, and ask the same series of questions and demand standard answers.

For people with Asperger syndrome any unexpected change in routine can be upsetting. Young children may impose their own routines, such as insisting on always walking the same route to school. At school, they may get upset by sudden changes such as an alteration to the timetable. People with Asperger syndrome often prefer to order their day according to a set pattern. If they work set hours then any unexpected delay, such as a traffic hold-up can make them anxious or upset.

Challenging behaviour

The person can also demonstrate challenging behaviour, such as running away, screaming, biting or kicking other people, grabbing things from counters in shops, socially unacceptable habits, or making naive and embarrassing remarks.

Special skills

About 10 per cent of children with autistic spectrum disorders have some special skill at a much higher level than the rest of their abilities – for example, music, art, numerical calculations or jigsaw puzzles.

Some have a remarkable memory for dates and things that particularly interest them. For example, people with Asperger syndrome often develop an almost obsessive interest in a hobby or collection. Usually their interest involves arranging or memorising facts about a specialist subject, such as train timetables, Derby winners, or the dimensions of cathedrals.

However, with encouragement, positive interests can be developed so that some go on to study or work in their favourite subjects.

Associated problems

A number of other problems are often associated with the triad:

- oversensitivity to all types of sensory input, especially sound
- poor motor co-ordination
- problems of attention and level of activity
- difficulties with eating, drinking and sleeping
- disturbance of mood.

Other disabilities associated with autistic spectrum disorders

Autistic spectrum disorders can occur in association with any other physical or psychological disability, such as cerebral palsy, Down's syndrome, dyslexia, a language disorder or generalised learning disability.

Epilepsy

Epilepsy occurs in about one-third of those with typical autism and is more common if there is also severe learning disability. Fits can begin in infancy, childhood, adolescence or even adult life. In some, the fits occur only with fever. Some teenagers might have one or two and then no more. Other children or adolescents have recurrent fits for many years or all their lives.

None of these conditions can 'explain away' autistic behaviour. If autism is present as well as another disability, it is essential that this is recognised, since it has important implications for treatment and prognosis. The task, is therefore to decide whether the triad of impairments also exists.

It is no use asking 'Is there autism or language disorder, deafness etc?' The question should always be: 'This child might have a language disorder, deafness etc. Does he or she also have the triad of impairments which characterises autism?'

The variety of presenting features

In looking out for signs, it is important to remember that features of the condition can vary widely from one child to another and there is no single feature that, if not present, excludes autism.

For example, a child with autism might make eye contact, speak with perfect grammar or put an arm round another child who is crying. Occasional behaviour of this kind does not exclude autism. It is the overall pattern that is relevant, not the intermittent flashes of 'normality'.

Age at presentation

Autistic spectrum disorders are lifelong. However, by the time of adolescence and adult life the differences between those with severe disabilities and those with an autistic spectrum disorder in a more subtle form will become clearer.

It is important to be aware that the more able person with an autistic spectrum disorder might not come to the GP at an older age and might never have had a diagnosis of any kind.

Early diagnosis

It is crucial that autism is recognised early in a child's life to enable effective intervention and management of the condition.

Early diagnosis and intervention is also essential to ensure families and carers have access to appropriate services and professional support.

Certainly the signs are there to be recognised. In most cases, the triad of impairments emerges in the first two to three years of life. Indeed, there are often indications of developmental problems within the first year. However, because autism is a complex condition it is easy to miss important clues.

Although the characteristics of autism are generally evident in the first few years of life, the conditions can go undetected for many years, especially in those who are at the more able end of the spectrum where the signs are more subtle.

People at the more able end of the spectrum are often aware that they are different from other people and that they have difficulty in forming or maintaining relationships. If undiagnosed their behaviour can appear odd, which can lead to bullying or teasing at school. Depression, therefore can be a feature as the person gets older.

Listening to parents

Sympathetic listening to parents and carers can provide a wealth of information. The following comments from parents could suggest that the child may have an autistic spectrum disorder:

- 'His speech is delayed, he's not talking. He doesn't respond to his name, could he be deaf?'
- 'She's not interested in playing with toys.'
- 'At the playgroup he won't have anything to do with the other children.'
- 'She hits other children if they get in her way.'
- 'He's not very affectionate, he doesn't like being touched and cuddled.'
- 'She clings to me all the time and won't let me out of her sight.'
- 'He insists on the same routine and is very upset if this is changed.'
- 'She seems very different from other children of her age.'
- 'At school he says nothing and gives no problems. At home he just won't fit in with the family.'
- 'She's always felt that she is different, which makes her angry and unhappy.'
- 'He seems to have no idea of how to follow the social rules.'

Diagnosing an autistic spectrum disorder – the difficulties

- The severity of the impairments differs from person to person.
- Different aspects of the behaviour pattern are more obvious at some ages than at others.
- The child's personality, education and social environment can markedly affect their behaviour.
- There can be other associated disabilities including epilepsy, cerebral palsy and sensory impairments.

What should be done if an autistic spectrum disorder is suspected?

If the presence of an autistic spectrum disorder is suspected, it is essential to refer the child, adolescent or adult for specialist diagnosis and assessment as early as possible.

For children, the first referral to confirm the diagnosis, made through the family doctor, is usually to the local paediatrician, child psychiatrist or child guidance clinic.

If you are a teacher, speak to other members of staff and the Special Educational Needs Advisor in your school. Make sure that they understand the child's behaviour and know what to expect.

Parents should find all the information and help they need through these local resources. If not, they have the right to ask for a second opinion.

There are a small number of centres in the UK that specialise in the diagnosis and assessment of children and adolescents with social and communication disorders. Some of these, including a service run by the NAS accept referrals of adults of all ages as well as children.

Help and training for GPs

If a local expert cannot be found, GPs can contact the NAS or The Centre for Social and Communication Disorders, which also provides training courses for professionals. They will be able to advise about the nearest source of expertise and help.

The NAS provides a wide range of services. This includes specific training for GPs through its training services department as part of the GP tutorial system.

NAS Training   Tel 0115 911 3363

The NAS Centre for Social and
  Communication Disorders   Tel 0181 466 0098

European Services for People with Autism Limited

E.S.P.A. is a Registered Charity affiliated to The National Autistic Society. We provide a range of services including residential care and further education in the North East of England for adults with Autism and Asperger's Syndrome.

E.S.P.A. is accredited with the FEFC (Further Education Funding Council) and is commended on the unique way in which students are supported to learn. Staff are highly trained and caring professionals experienced in Autism Spectrum Disorders.

Our aim is to nurture self-awareness and independence as well as providing appropriate educational experiences through an inclusive learning package.

For further information and a brochure contact:

E.S.P.A. Ltd
9 The Cedars
Ashbrooke
Sunderland
SR2 7TW

Tel: 0191 5673523 Fax: 0191 514 3858

Registered Charity No.1037868   Company No. 2909953

WARGRAVE HOUSE SCHOOL
449 Wargrave Road
Newton-le-Willows
Merseyside, WA12 8RS

Principal: Mrs. Pam Maddock B.Ed (Hons) DIP. T.O.M.H.

Tel: 01925 224899   Fax: 01925 291368

"This is a very good school with many outstanding features"

"The ethos of the school is excellent"
(OFSTED Report;)

Wargrave House is a day and weekly boarding independent school with a population of 62 mixed ability pupils who have autistic spectrum disorder. The school has a Further Education Unit for students between the ages of 16 and 19. The catchment area is the North West of England.

The school's ethos is centred around the belief in strong partnership with parents/carers and shared aims and practical cooperation draws on this breadth of intimate knowledge and expertise.

We incorporate a functional and pragmatic approach to learning which is concerned with both the process and the product of education.

SECTION Va

For teachers

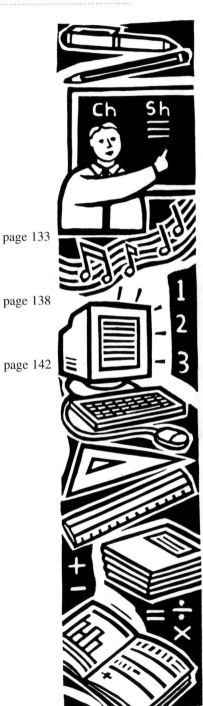

Chapter 16

Teaching children with autistic spectrum disorders in mainstream primary schools

Rosemary Siddles, NAS Education Advisor

Introduction

As a teacher the chances are you'll meet several children with autism or Asperger syndrome in the course of your career. While some people with autism will always need care and supervision, with practice many can improve and develop their social, communication and academic skills. This means that everything you do to help is a step in the right direction.

If a child with an autistic spectrum disorder does not require special education, then they are unlikely to have obvious learning disabilities. But they will have special needs.

There are many ways you can help them by adapting your teaching.

SPELL

The acronym SPELL describes the necessary environment and support system which enables the child with autistic spectrum disorders to learn. The approach also minimises stress.

Structure helps the child to make sense of a very confusing world. It can help to provide a predictable and 'safe' world through the reduction of some of the unexpected or unpredictable events. Carefully planned and evaluated structure leads to the child becoming independent, rather than over-dependent in an entirely prompt-led culture.

Positive attitudes and appropriately pitched expectation enhance the child's self esteem and self confidence. Working with, and building upon the child's special interests and strengths can be a valuable teaching strategy.

Empathy Seeing the world from the child's unique viewpoint and aiming to understand his/her perceptions demands empathy. It is necessary to design a differentiated, individualised programme for the child.

Low arousal The child's learning environment needs to be clear, calm and clutter free. A stress-reducing environment integrates opportunity for relaxation and energetic activity. Potentially stressful or aversive tasks can be released in a supportive manner, thus reducing anxiety.

In the classroom

To determine strategies for use in teaching, you will need to explore the variety of ways in which structure can be provided to support the child's learning, while ensuring the child does not become prompt dependent. A separate workstation may be a consideration. The 'workstation' could be a small table flanked by two bookcases, providing privacy and freedom from unnecessary distraction.

Careful attention needs to be paid to the whole learning environment. Is it sufficiently free of distraction without being isolating? Can the child find all necessary resources – will he/she benefit from visual prompts, such as pictures, picture symbols, diagrams, graphs or written instructions? A personal timetable at the workstation, or carried in a diary can be a useful prompt for teacher, parent and child.

Can the child access adult support in an acceptable manner? How does he/she indicate they have finished their work – should you agree a 'code' word? Some children benefit from the use of a timer to indicate the end of an activity.

Does he/she need a little extra support in the group setting? Learning Support Assistant (LSA) support, which might be a presence or verbal support, can be useful in group situations (such as the Literacy Hour, assembly or newstime!)

Is the timetable or work schedule easy to understand? A personal timetable may be easier to understand accompanied by photographs or symbols.

Some children have difficulties with writing – do you need to persevere – could he/she not use a wordprocessor? Consider teaching a cursive style of writing from the beginning.

Breaktime (morning or afternoon)

Some children may benefit from structure at breaktimes. They may not play 'naturally' and the deliberate teaching of playground activities may be useful. Other children will need visual supervision. Dependency upon a supervision assistant should be carefully monitored. Some children benefit from a paired 'buddy' during breaktimes.

Lunchtime

Lunchtime breaks can last from 30 minutes to an hour, and are often extremely stressful times for children with autistic spectrum disorders. Just as in other school-based activities this time needs to be carefully planned, and some role playing of segments of the break could be of benefit, ie queuing for lunch, choosing food. Choice may be a difficult issue for some children and in this instance a menu plan from home may be the best arrangement.

Just as during the shorter breaktimes, the freetime after the meal may need to be structured for the child. Some schools can arrange for children experiencing difficulties with long breaks to work inside.

Play

This can be an area of difficulty for children with autistic spectrum disorders, but it is not appropriate to deprive them of the opportunity to explore play and to experience play with others. Given free choice the child may choose to repeat activities. They may apparently have little curiosity about their environment, and it may be useful to prompt before playtime, or teach skills via role playing of activities. It is useful to use organised playtime to teach sharing, co-operation, social rules and turn taking. As in breaktimes a befriender or 'buddy' may be a useful enabler.

Working with parents

Children with autistic spectrum disorders do not readily communicate the day's activities as so many other children do. A home-school journal is a useful communication tool and a few sentences are all that is necessary. Working with parents and agreeing common strategies and targets are essential. Consistent practice is vital.

For those children who are statemented, the annual review is an ideal opportunity to talk at length regarding the child's needs and IEP. Similar time needs to be set aside to agree targets and strategies for those who are not statemented but have this complex disorder.

Bullying

Children with autistic spectrum disorders are ready targets for bullying. They are vulnerable and very sensitive. There are many examples of these children refusing to go to school because of bullying, some of which is quite subtle. Any hint of bullying should be addressed and taken seriously. The school will have a policy for its management.

The National Autistic Society (NAS) Training Services Department

Training Professionals and carers for today and tomorrow

We are able to provide autism specific training for professionals and carers throughout the UK. During 1999 we are planning to run a series of conferences, seminars and workshops on a range of topics. We also provide tailored "in house" training for statutory, voluntary and private organisations.

Topics will include:

> SPELL Framework. Both 1 and 2 day workshops. This is a new initiative by the NAS, based on many years experience in our own schools and units.

> TEACCH. Both a 1 day 'Introduction to the principles of TEACCH', as well as the 3 day workshop on 'Structured Teaching Model: Basic Concepts'.

We will also be providing our normal programme that could include:

- What is Autism?
- Addressing the Triad of Impairments
- Challenging Behaviour
- Autism in Mainstream Schools
- Autism in Special Schools
- Asperger's Syndrome in Children
- Adults with Asperger's Syndrome

THE NATIONAL AUTISTIC SOCIETY

For further information, please contact

The National Autistic Society, Training Services Department,
2nd Floor, Castle Heights, 72 Maid Marian Way, Nottingham NG1 6BJ.
Tel: 0115 911 3363   Fax: 0115 911 3362
E mail: training@nas.org.uk

Chapter 17

Teaching children with autistic spectrum disorders in mainstream secondary schools

Rosemary Siddles, NAS Education Advisor

Introduction

The transition for children with autistic spectrum disorders from primary to secondary school may be very difficult. The child will be required (in the new school setting) to generalise, to reflect, to analyse, interpret and extrapolate: all processes which he/she will find hard, or impossible, to do.

In addition, the social interaction of a busy secondary school may be too much for the child to tolerate. Some children with autistic spectrum disorders do manage in the mainstream setting given appropriate support and understanding from staff.

Role of the SENco

The Special Educational Needs co-ordinator (SENco) plays a central role in co-ordinating effective provision for pupils with special needs. The SENco will maintain the central records and liaise with parents. The SENco needs to monitor the training of the teaching team regarding any pupils with autistic spectrum disorders.

The SENco is also the pivotal person in bringing together other agency representatives, ie speech therapist, psychiatrist, psychologists and others.

It is the class/subject teacher's responsibility to devise individual programmes and ensure that the curriculum is differentiated.

Timetable

Just as with younger children the teacher's requirements for the pupil must be transparent. A visual timetable with essential information according to the individual needs (room number, name of subject teachers, breaktimes etc) will be very helpful. The timetable can usefully be carried in a personal organiser diary complete with school rules, personally negotiated rules/contracts, homework requirements etc.

Free time

Free time may be difficult for some of these pupils to cope with, and use of that time should be discussed with the pupil. Such support may be necessary throughout the whole of the pupil's time at the school. Choice can be a difficult issue and may have to be managed between teacher and pupil, the teacher giving a written list of free time activities and the pupil selecting them with the teacher's guidance.

A mentor may be useful, in addition to a pastoral tutor as these communication activities can take up quite a bit of time. These young people are very vulnerable and misuse of free time with pupils gravitating unsupervised to inappropriate activities can become a habit which is difficult to break. Typically, pupils with autistic spectrum disorders lack the motivation to do much for themselves, save that which might be described as their special interest.

Homework

It needs to be made clear from the beginning that homework is a requirement, written into the timetable, and respected as a school rule. Children with autistic spectrum disorders often find it difficult to do work associated with school at home (and vice versa). It may be better for some pupils to stay after the school day and complete homework in a 'homework club'. It is quite likely that the minimum requirement only will be met and any more will need to be specifically requested.

PE

Pupils with autistic spectrum disorders can frequently transfer to secondary school with poor PE skills, as very often they have little stamina and a poor level of fitness. They may suffer poor co-ordination and consequently can be very embarrassed by their difficulties. Many of these pupils will have difficulties in understanding team games and the need for co-operation and game strategy. On the other hand, there is no reason why they should not succeed in such activities as dance, athletics, golf and other activities where they perform 'alone'.

Social behaviour

Some pupils may appear rude, opinionated and abrupt. They are very likely to have few, if any, friends and may be attracted to those pupils who exhibit antisocial behaviour. Social skills need to be taught and again role play is a useful strategy.

Working with parents

As with younger children, there is a continued need to work in close collaboration with parents. Even as young adults, pupils with autistic spectrum disorders are not likely to communicate readily about school activities with their parents. The organiser diary (see 'Timetable') may be a useful communication tool. Targets and strategies will need to be agreed with parents/carers throughout the pupil's school career. This form of working is commonly associated with much younger children and, for the teacher, will take much adjustment but it is relevant and necessary.

Bullying

This group of young people is highly susceptible to bullying and this can be well hidden in the secondary school. Here the relationship of the mentor or pastoral teacher is important in maintaining an open exchange with the pupil.

Transfer

The issue of any transfer is difficult for this group of young people, but more so upon leaving school. However apparently able and sophisticated the pupil may appear, the transfer should be managed with attention to detail and involve all pupil contact workers and parents in the process.

Chapter 18

Resources

*Items available from the Publications Department have a (P) listed after
the title or if they are available from the Information Centre you will find a
(I) listed after the title. To obtain copies, please refer to the Publications
List (Section VI of this Handbook) or for articles available from the
Information Centre please write to the Information Centre at The National
Autistic Society, 393 City Road, London EC1V 1NG. Please note that book
prices are correct at the time of print but these may be subject to change.*

Cummie, V, Leach, J and Stevenson, G (1998) **Asperger syndrome, a
practical guide for teachers** David Fulton Publishers £14 (P)
This is a clear and concise guide to effective classroom practice for
teachers and support assistants working with children with Asperger
syndrome in mainstream schools and other non-specialist settings. This
book seeks to inform and equip professionals meeting a child with
Asperger syndrome for the first time with effective educational and
behavioural strategies.

Leicester City Council and Leicestershire County Council (1998) **Asperger
syndrome – practical strategies for the classroom: a teacher's guide**.
The National Autistic Society £8.99 (P)
Primarily for teachers, this practical booklet is divided into six areas where
difficulties may arise for the child with Asperger syndrome; social

interaction, communication, imagination, sensory/motor difficulties, emotional difficulties and work skills. The contents lists the type of behaviours a pupil may present and directs the teacher to the relevant section.

Jordan, R and Powell, S (1997) **Autism and learning: a guide to good practice** David Fulton Publishers £13.99 plus p&p (P)
This books shows how a cognitive perspective on the way in which individuals with autism think and learn, may be applied to particular curriculum ideas.

Jordan, R and Powell, S (1995) **Understanding and teaching children with autism** John Wiley £18.99 plus p&p (P)
Practical guidance based on the premise that effective teaching must be rooted in a firm understanding of autism and the fundamental impairments associated with it.

Jordan, R and Powell, S (1990) **The special curricular needs of autistic children: learning and thinking skills** The Association of Heads & Teachers of Adults and Children with Autism £2.50 plus p&p (P)
Specifically concentrates upon the challenges which are presented to educators in developing the cognitive skills of children with autism.

Timetable for autism (1997) The National Autistic Society 50p plus p&p (P)
An overview of educating children and young people with autistic spectrum disorders.

The Education of children with autism Free information sheet (I)

Kemp, D **Children and young persons with special educational needs – assessment and recording**. The Scottish Office Education and Industry Department, Area 2A (West), Victoria Quay, Edinburgh EH6 6QQ.

Autistic spectrum disorders – a guide for schools (1998) The National Autistic Society. Individual copies free from the Publications Department (P)
This booklet gives an introduction on some of the issues involved in educating a pupil with autism or Asperger syndrome.

Friel, J (1995) **Young adults with special needs: assessment, law and practice**. Jessica Kingsley
A handbook for parents, carers and people working with young people with special needs and covers the assessment of and procedure for young adults with special needs. Includes information on the 1992 Further and Higher Education Act and the 1993 Education Act.

SECTION Vb

For GPs and other health professionals

Chapter 19

Understanding the family

Dr Cathie Scothorne, GP

In an average list size of 2,000 patients, each GP may have up to 18 people on the autistic spectrum on his/her list[1]. Autistic spectrum disorders may be regarded as a low incidence disorder which, unlike for example hypertension, has no obvious active role for a GP. However, the role of the GP can be vitally important, particularly in the early stages of diagnosis and adjustment to that diagnosis.

Identifying the problem

Parents may present with problems in their children in all sorts of ways. Often a concern about development will not be the primary presenting feature in a consultation. The non-specific and variable nature of the autistic spectrum does not make it easy for a parent to identify a problem. It is easier to describe a pain in a leg than a feeling that something is not quite right.

There may well have been an anxiety that all is not well with a child for some time. However, as a parent we can all justify behavioural patterns which mark our child out as different – 'he's a boy', 'he's the second child', 'his father was just the same'. We do not wish to find problems in our children.

---

1 Estimated prevalence rate of people with autistic spectrum disorders in the UK is 91 people in every 10,000.

Well meaning reassurance by relatives and friends may compound the delay in presentation. If, when a concern is eventually raised it is dismissed with no obvious detailed assessment, considerable resentment and a feeling of isolation and despair soon build up.

GPs need to be aware that even from a very early age, eg 18 months, use of diagnostic aids, such as CHAT can give some indication as to whether there are indeed grounds for concern[2]. As professionals we have a responsibility to be well informed so that, after listening carefully to the anxieties presented to us, we may act appropriately. Reassurance that development is within the norm may well be appropriate. However, we must all be aware of our limitations and such reassurance must be based on an adequate history and examination and assessment as in all our medical practice. GPs must have access to a secondary referral centre with proven expertise in the assessment of child development. Many parents feel obliged to seek a tertiary referral because of lack of local expertise.

Assessment

Once referral to a secondary centre has been made, both parents and GP must be fully aware of what the assessment process will entail. Parents can accept that at an early age, children may need to be monitored over a period of time before a firm diagnosis is made. There must be an opportunity for parents to discuss possible diagnoses during this time with professionals who have the knowledge and counselling skills to do so.

The professionals involved in the assessment should work together closely as a team with a key worker clearly identified. Parents often feel bewildered by the involvement of many professionals and are often unsure who to approach for information. Many return to their GP at this stage. The GP should be in the position of being fully informed as to the progress of the

2 The checklist for Autism and Toddlers (CHAT) is used as a screening process to identify children with autism, and has been developed by a team at Cambridge University and Guy's Hospital in London. It provides a series of questions to be used by GPs, health visitors and parents to discover if the young child ever points at objects and people to indicate interest, or engages in imaginative play – behaviours absent in most children with autism.

assessment by liaising with the key worker. Parents will then remain confident that their case is in good hands.

Anxieties

Any parent of a child with a problem will have anxieties: about the nature of the problem and its short and long term implications; about day to day management; and about reactions of siblings, relations and friends. This may well be compounded by feeding and sleeping problems so prevalent in children on the autistic spectrum. These anxieties need to be acknowledged, and, where possible, practical advice given. Although a clear-cut diagnosis may not be possible, this does not mean that professionals are unable to support and advise the family in behavioural management while assessment is in progress.

Many families feel that they are left dangling in mid-air, all management plans being delayed until a firm diagnosis is made. Achieving a diagnosis then becomes an overwhelming priority for the families since it appears as if it is the golden ticket to all the treatment/management programmes the child may require. Imagine how it must feel to believe that you are being denied a diagnosis and, by implication, the route to help for your child. It is easy to understand why many parents feel relieved when a diagnosis is made. It may not be until later that the full implications begin to take their toll.

Making a diagnosis

Some professionals feel that there is a considerable resistance to 'labelling'. This may indeed be so. However, this may be partly because of concerns about the quality of assessment and subsequent diagnosis. There are also fears that the label may hinder, rather than help, the child in their future relationships and education. As health professionals we have a responsibility to make the correct diagnosis. We also have a responsibility to educate and advise parents, relatives, friends and the community as a whole about autism. We need to break down the false barriers between the responsibilities of health, education and social services. Once a diagnosis is made parents need to feel that there is an integrated approach between these services. Autistic spectrum disorder is a condition which can soon make even the most competent of parents feel overwhelmed. There is no justification for professionals dismissing their potential involvement by stating 'it is an education not a health problem.'

The disability generates anxiety in patients, parents, the community and professionals. This must be recognised and addressed. Often parents find the professionals sadly lacking in their knowledge. Parents often become extremely well informed by extensive reading, listening to the radio/TV and involvement in self support groups. This should not make a GP feel inadequate, threatened or without a role. GPs have good background knowledge of families and the communities in which they live. GPs spend a considerable amount of their time looking after patients with long term illness. They are well trained and experienced in this field and have many resources available to them. There is no reason why these skills and resources should not be applicable to families affected by this disorder. Families need continued support and care to enable them to approach their child and their future in the most positive way.

Chapter 20

Resources

Items available from the Publications Department have a (P) listed after the title or if they are available from the Information Centre you will find a (I) listed after the title. To obtain copies, please refer to the Publications List (Section VI of this Handbook) or for articles available from the Information Centre please write to the Information Centre at The National Autistic Society, 393 City Road, London EC1V 1NG. Please note that book prices are correct at the time of print but these may be subject to change.

Ellis, K (editor) (1990) ***Autism: professional perspectives and practice.*** Chapman and Hall £18.50 plus p&p (P)
Written by a team of recognised experts, this book will prepare all those who work with people with autism for the various stages they will go through including the initial diagnosis, education and practical care.

Happé, F (1994) ***Autism: an introduction to psychological theory.*** UCL Press £13.95 plus p&p (P)
An essential scientific introduction for all those studying autism in psychology, medicine, speech science and education at undergraduate level and above, as well as an enlightening read for both parents and carers of children with autism.

Howlin, P and Moore, A (1997) **'Diagnosis in autism: a survey of over 1,200 patients in the UK'** *Autism* Vol 1(2) pp135-162. (I)
The results of a survey of almost 1,300 parent members of autistic societies in the UK are described. The survey focused on parents' views of the diagnostic process and data were collected on the age at which diagnosis was made, the time taken to obtain a diagnosis and the professionals involved.

The National Autistic Society (1995) *Could this be autism?* 50p plus p&p (P)
A more substantial booklet aimed at stimulating awareness of autism, explaining the condition and highlighting the signs to look out for. Aimed at everyone working in health, education and social care.

O'Hare, A, E , Quew, R and Aitken, K (1998) **'The identification of autism in children referred to a tertiary speech and language clinic and the implications for service delivery'** *Autism* Vol 2(2) pp171-180. (I)
The Edinburgh Children's Hospital speech clinic is a joint paediatric and speech therapy clinic which was first established in 1950 and accepts referral of children for whom speech and language difficulties are the principal concern. An audit was conducted for children presenting consecutively over January 1993 to January 1994 to identify what proportion of these children had autism and related disorders.

Schopler, E and Mesibov, G (Ed) (1988) *Diagnosis and assessment in autism* Plenum

Smith, B et al (1994) **'The path to care in autism: is it better now?'** *Journal of autism and developmental disorders* 24(5) pp551-563
Parents of children with autism often report problems associated with obtaining a diagnosis of their child's condition, family support, information and appropriate services. To evaluate any changes in the situation over the last two decades, the families of all members of the West Midlands Autistic Society, aged 19 years and below, were asked to fill in a questionnaire that covered aspects of detection, diagnosis, help and information received and educational provision.

Volkmar, F, R (1998) '**Categorical approaches to the diagnosis of autism: an overview of DSM-IV and ICD-10**' *Autism* Vol 2(1) pp 45-59. (I)
Although autism was first reported in 1943 nearly 40 years elapsed before the disorder was included as an official diagnosis in the American (DSM) classification system. In the last two decades guidelines for the diagnosis of this, and related, conditions have evolved based on a growing body of research. An important recent development has been the convergence of the American (DSM) and International (ICD) diagnostic systems. Although these two official systems differ somewhat in format and intended use, the advent of consistent approaches to the diagnosis of autism will facilitate both research and clinical service. Data that have informed the development of these systems are reviewed and areas of continuing controversy are noted.

SECTION VI

Publications

Chapter 21

Publications

All the books that are available from the NAS Publications Department that have been mentioned in the Resources sections of this Handbook are listed below. If you wish to order them, please fill in the form enclosed and send this, together with payment to: The National Autistic Society Publications, 393 City Road, London, EC1V 1NG. Alternatively, if your order is above £5 you can order with a credit card by phoning 0171 903 3595. Please note that book prices are correct at the time of print but these may be subject to change.

Post and packing

Post and packing are not included in the prices shown. Using the table provided on p159, please add the appropriate postage and packaging to the total price of the publications. Please note that post and packing are dependent upon the weight of the order and if the standard charge is insufficient, a further charge may be applied.

Discounts

Please note that all NAS members are entitled to a 10% discount on NAS publications. This is indicated by a '%' sign after the title of the book. If this appears and you are an NAS member, please deduct 10% off the unit price of the publication.

SECTION 2: AUTISTIC SPECTRUM DISORDERS

Author/Title	Price	Code	Qty
Aarons & Gittens **The handbook of autism: a guide for parents and professionals**	£13.99	109	
Attwood **Asperger's syndrome: a guide for parents and professionals**	£12.95	246	
Baron-Cohen & Bolton **Autism: the facts**	£8.99	104	
Frith **Autism and Asperger syndrome**	£15.95	101	
Gilpin **Laughing and loving with autism**	£6	243	
The National Autistic Society **Autism: the invisible children?** %	£4.99	05	
Tantum **A mind of one's own** %	£1.99	46	
Williams **Autism: an inside-out approach**	£14.95	221	
Wing **Autistic spectrum disorders: an aid to diagnosis** %	£1.99	16	
Wing **The autistic spectrum: a guide for parents and professionals**	£16.95	216	

SECTION 3: FOR PARENTS

Education

Author/Title	Price	Code	Qty
Jordan & Powell **Understanding and teaching children with autism**	£18.99	120	
Jordan & Powell **Autism and learning: a guide to good practice**	£13.99	229	
The National Autistic Society **The autistic spectrum: a parent's guide** %	£2	260	
The National Autistic Society **Schools, units and classes for children with autism** %	£2.99	56	
The National Autistic Society **Timetable for autism** %	50p	250	

Daily living skills

Author/Title	Price	Code	Qty
Dickenson and Hannah **It can get better** %	£5	02	
Leicestershire County Council and Fosse Health Trust **Autism: how to help your young child** %	£8.99	247	
Schopler (Ed) **Parent survival manual**	£21.99	231	

Autism and adulthood

Author/Title	Price	Code	Qty
Attwood **Why does Chris do that?** %	£3.99	66	
Howlin **Preparing for adulthood**	£14.99	228	
Morgan **Adults with autism: a guide to theory and practice**	£24.95	225	
Mortlock **The socio-sexual development of people with autism and related learning disabilities** %	£1.25	58	
The Inge Wakehurst Trust **Adolescents and adults with Asperger syndrome** %	£4.99	11	
The Inge Wakehurst Trust **Adolescents and adults with autism** %	£4.99	01	

SECTION 4: FOR PEOPLE WITH AUTISTIC SPECTRUM DISORDERS

Author/Title	Price	Code	Qty
Asperger United (UK)	£4		
Asperger United (Overseas)	£6		
Grandin **Emergence labelled autistic**	£9.99	107	
Grandin **Thinking in pictures**	£9.99	108	
Howlin **Preparing for adulthood**	£14.99	228	
Williams **Nobody nowhere**	£6.99	114	
Williams **Somebody somewhere**	£6.99	119	
Williams **Like colour to the blind**	£15.99	226	

SECTION 5: FOR PROFESSIONALS

For teachers

Author/Title	Price	Code	Qty
Cummie et al **Asperger syndrome, a practical guide for teachers**	£14	257	
Leicester City Council and Leicestershire County Council **Asperger syndrome – practical strategies for the classroom** %	£8.99	255	
Jordan and Powell **Autism and learning: a guide to good practice**	£13.99	229	
Jordan and Powell **Understanding and teaching children with autism**	£18.99	120	
Jordan and Powell **The special curricular needs of autistic children: learning and thinking skills**	£2.50	61	
The National Autistic Society **Timetable for autism** %	50p	250	
The National Autistic Society **Autistic spectrum disorders: a guide for schools**	Free	207	

For GPs and other health professionals

Author/Title	Price	Code	Qty
Ellis **Autism: professional perspective and practice**	£18.50	103	
Happé **Autism: an introduction to psychological theory**	£13.95	105	
The National Autistic Society **Could this be autism?** %	50p	214	

Postage and Packaging

Orders up to £5 - add 75p
up to £10 - add £1.50
up to £20 - add £2.50
up to £40 - add £3.50
over £70 - add £7.50
Overseas orders - please add
25% of invoice total.

TOTAL PRICE	£
POST AND PACKING	£
DONATION (Optional)	£
GRAND TOTAL	£

Your details

Methods of payment

Payment should accompany your order. We are happy to accept cheques, postal orders and credit cards.

Please print clearly

Organisation ....

Contact name Mr/Mrs/Ms ....

Address ....

Town..

County ....

Postcode .... Telephone ....

NAS member   Yes   ❏   No   ❏

Are you a student/professional/parent/other (please specify)

....

I enclose a cheque/postal order made payable to:

The National Autistic Society   ❏

Please debit my Access/Visa/MasterCard card   ❏

No | | | | | | | | | | | | | | | | |

Expiry date   ....

Total amount   ....

Signature .... Date ....

Please allow 21 days for delivery

SECTION VII

Useful contacts

Chapter 22

The National Autistic Society

Head Office
393 City Road, London EC1V 1NG
Switchboard: 0171 833 2299
Fax: 0171 833 9666
E-mail: nas@nas.org.uk
Web site:
http://www.oneworld.org/autism_uk/

Autism Helpline: 0171 903 3555
E-mail: autismhelpline@nas.org.uk

This is a written and telephone
enquiry service with the phone line
open between 10 – 11.30 am and 2 –
3.30 pm weekdays – offers advice
and support to parents, carers and
people with autism and Asperger
syndrome.

Fundraising: 0171 903 3522

Information: 0171 903 3599
E-mail: informationcentre@nas.org.uk

This is a written and telephone
enquiry service with the phone line
open between 10 am and 4 pm
weekdays – offers information and
advice on all aspects of autism, NAS
services and related topics to
professionals, students, researchers
and voluntary organisations. In
addition there is a library that parents
and researchers can use by
appointment only.

Press: 0171 903 3593
E-mail: press@nas.org.uk

**Prospects: Supported Employment
Service:** 0171 903 3597

Prospects is a supported employment
service for adults with autism and
Asperger syndrome.

Publications: 0171 903 3595
E-mail: publications@nas.org.uk

The Publications Department has one
of the best lists on autism and
Asperger syndrome in the country –
catalogues will be sent out on request.

Scottish Office
Suite 3, 111 Union Street
Glasgow
Strathclyde G1 3TA
Tel: 0141 221 8090
Fax: 0141 221 8118

Welsh Office
William Knox House, Suite C1,
Britannic Way, Llandarcy
Neath
West Glamorgan SA10 6EL
Tel: 01792 815915
Fax: 01792 815911

Services Division
Church House
Church Road
Filton
Bristol
BS34 7BD
Tel: 0117 987 2575
Fax: 0117 987 2576

For details of NAS schools and adult
centres

Development and Outreach and Training
Castle Heights
4th Floor
72 Maid Marian Way
Nottingham
NG1 6BJ
Tel: 0115 911 3360
Fax: 0115 911 2259

Training
Tel: 0115 911 3363
Fax: 0115 911 3362
E-mail: training@nas.org.uk

Training Services offers various
courses for parents and professionals
relating to the autistic spectrum.
Tailor-made courses are also available
to groups.

Volunteers co-ordination
Tel: 0115 911 3369
Fax: 0115 911 3362
E-mail: volunteers@nas.org.uk

The Volunteering Network co-
ordinates nationwide parent to parent
and befriending schemes. The
schemes are available to parents of
people with autistic spectrum
disorders.

The Centre for Social and Communication Disorders
Elliot House
113 Masons Hill
Bromley
Kent
BR2 9HT
Tel: 0181 466 0098
Fax: 0181 466 0118

Chapter 23

Other useful organisations

Benefits and financial help

Information on claiming DLA or any other welfare benefit can be obtained by contacting your local Citizens Advice Bureau or from:

The Disability Alliance
1st Floor, Universal House
88-94 Wentworth St
London E1 7SA
Rights Advice line 0171 247 8763
(Monday and Wednesday 2-4 pm)

The Disability Benefit Enquiry Line
Tel 0800 882200
(Monday - Friday 8.30 am - 6.30 pm and Saturday 9 am - 1 pm)

The Family Fund
PO Box 50
York
YO2 2ZX

The Family Fund was set up to help families caring for disabled children. They can give help, depending on circumstances, with a range of issues.

Counselling and Psychology

The British Association of Counselling
Tel: 01788 550899

The Association will provide a list of accredited counsellors working in particular regions across the country.

British Psychological Society
St Andrew's House
48 Princess Road East
Leicester LE1 7DR
Tel.: 0116 254 9568
Fax: 0116 247 0787
E-mail: mail@bps.org.uk
Website: http://www.bps.org.uk

The Society maintains an annual register of chartered psychologists. A useful organisation to contact for information and literature.

UK Council for Psychotherapy
Tel: 0171 436 3002

The Council will provide names of psychotherapists working in different areas.

Education

ACE (Advisory Centre for Education)
1B Aberdeen Studios
22-24 Highbury Grove
London N5 2DQ
Advice Line: 0171 354 8321 (2-5 pm Monday-Friday)

National independent education advice service. ACE also publishes a magazine, information sheets and handbooks.

CSIE (Centre for Studies on Inclusive Education)
1 Redland Close
Elm Lane
Redland
Bristol BS6 6UE
Tel: 0117 923 8450

CSIE publishes a range of leaflets and reports, runs a free advice service and organises courses and conferences.

Independent Panel for Special Education Advice (IPSEA)
4 Ancient House Mews
Woodbridge
Suffolk IP12 1DH

Parent Advice Line: 01394 382814
IPSEA aims to provide parents with expert second opinions and independent advice on the special educational needs of their children. IPSEA also runs a free representation service to support parents who want to appeal to the new Special Educational Needs Tribunal.

ISIS (Independent Schools Information Service)
56 Buckingham Gate
London SW1E 6AG
Tel: 0171 630 8793

ISIS provides information, help and advice to parents choosing an independent school.

National Portage Association
Brenda Paul - Administrator
127 Monks Dale
Yeovil BA21 3JE
Tel/Fax: 01935 471641

Network '81
1-7 Woodfield Terrace
Stansted
Essex CM24 8AJ
Helpline: 01279 647415
(10 am - 12 pm Monday - Friday)

A national network of parents of children with special educational needs. Provides a helpline service and produces a range of literature.

Royal College of Speech and Language Therapists
7 Bath Place
Rivington Street
London EC2A 3DR
Tel: 0171 613 3855
Fax: 0171 613 3854

Government Departments

Department for Education and Employment (DFEE)
Sanctuary Buildings
Great Smith St
London SW1P 3BT
Tel: 0171 925 5000

Welsh Office
Schools Administration
Division 3, Phase 2
Government Buildings
Ty Glas Road
Llanishen
Cardiff CF4 5WE
Tel: 01222 761456

Scotland
The Scottish Office
Education Department
New St Andrew's House
Regent Road
Edinburgh EH1 3TG
Tel: 0131 556 8400

Northern Ireland
Northern Ireland Office
Department of Education and Industry
Special Education Branch
Rattigael House
Balloo Road
Bangor
County Down BT19 7PR
Tel: 01247 279000

Legal

The Children's Legal Centre
The University of Essex
Wivenhoe Park
Colchester
Essex CO4 3SQ
Advice line: 01206 873820

Advice service on all aspects of law and policies which affect children and young people.

The Law Society
113 Chancery lane
London WC2A 1PL
Tel: 0171 242 1222

The Law Society publishes a list of solicitors who do legal aid work and provides information on other sources of legal advice.

Support Organisations

Association to aid the sexual and personal relationships of people with a disability (SPOD)
286 Camden Road
London N7 0BJ
Tel: 0171 607 8851

Contact a Family
Tel: 0171 383 3555

Contact a family is an umbrella organisation that puts people in touch with support networks throughout the country.

The Council for Disabled Children
8 Wakely St
London EC1V 7QE
Tel: 0171 843 6061

The Council publishes a wide range of lists, fact sheets on special educational needs.

Disabled Childrens Foundation
11/23 Royal Chambers
110 Station Parade
Harrogate
North Yorkshire HG1 1EP
Tel: 01423 509863

This organisation can help with specialised equipment.

Holiday Care Service
2nd Floor
Imperial Buildings
Victoria Road
Horley
Surrey RH6 7PZ
Tel: 01293 774535

Provides free information on holidays for people with special needs. The service also produces a booklet on holiday and short break accommodation, suitable for carers, either travelling alone or with a person with a disability.

In Touch Trust
10 Norman Road
Sale M33 3DF
Tel: 0161 905 2440
Fax: 0161 718 5787
Puts parents of children with rare conditions in touch with each other. Gives information on support groups.

MENCAP
123 Golden Lane
London EC1Y 0RT
Tel: 0171 454 0454
Mencap is a national organisation for children and adults with learning disabilities. There are also local branches across the country.

National Association of Citizens Advice Bureaux
115-123 Pentoville Road
London N1 9LZ
Tel: 0171 833 2181

The Bureaux's head office will provide details of local Citizen Advice Bureaux which offer information and advice on a wide range of subjects.

RADAR (Royal Association for Disability and Rehabilitation)
12 City Forum
250 City Road
London EV1V 8AF
Tel: 0171 250 3222

Shared Care UK
Norah Fry Research Centre
3 Priory Road
Bristol BS8 1TX
Tel: 0117 946 7230

For information about respite care

SKILL (National Bureau for Students with Disabilities)
336 Brixton Road
London SW9 8RR
Tel: 0171 978 9890 (1.30 - 4.30 pm Monday - Friday)

Information and advice on education, training, support services etc for young people aged 16+.

Web sites for people with autistic spectrum disorders

Website maintained by people with autism and Asperger syndrome
http://amug.org/na203/index.html

This is an excellent site for peer support, forums and self-help strategies. The site is maintained by people with autism/Asperger syndrome.

Autism Network International
http://www.students.uiuc.edu/~bordner/ani.html

This is a self-advocacy group run by and for autistic people. The group welcomes families but the main focus is on the issues and needs of individuals on the autistic spectrum.

Independent Living Forums
http://www.inlv.demon.nl/

These are a series of support lists/forums for individuals with autism/Asperger syndrome and related disorders.

University Students with autism and Asperger syndrome
http://www.users.dircon.co.uk/~cns/index.html

This page was put together by a university student who has Asperger syndrome and is for other students with Asperger syndrom and autism.

#Asperger
http://www.nox.com/asp/asp.htm

This channel is only for those individuals who are on the autistic spectrum and provides a safe place to communicate and meet others. There are links to other channels for parents and professionals.

Chapter 24

The Autism Services Accreditation Register

The Autism Service Accreditation Programme was set up in 1993 by the NAS in association with affiliated local autistic societies. The programme operates as an independent service to ensure consistent standards are achieved whether the care service is provided by the NAS, a local society, a local authority or another independent organisation. Listed below are all the services (at the time of writing - October 1998) that are registered with the programme.

Schools (in alphabetic order)

Broomhayes School
(an NAS school)
Kingsley House
Alverdiscott Road
Bideford
North Devon EX39 4PL
Tel: 01237 473830

Camphill Rudolf Steiner Schools
Murtle Estate
Bieldside
Aberdeen
AB1 9EP
Tel: 01224 867935

The Children's Service
(Community Health Services NHS
Trust, Southern Derbyshire)
104 Broadway
Derby
DE22 1BP
Tel: 01332 347592

Church Hill School (independent)
The Old Rectory
Church Hill
Banham
Norfolk
NR16 2HN
Tel: 01953 887815

Daldorch House School
(an NAS school)
Sorn Road
Catrine
East Ayrshire KA5 6NA
Tel: 01290 551666

Doucecroft School
(an Essex Autistic Society school)
163 High St
Kelvedon
Colchester
Essex CO5 9JA
Tel: 01376 570060

Green Hedges School
(a Cambridgeshire County Council
school)
Bar Lane
Stapleford
Cambridge
CB2 5BJ
Tel: 01223 508608

The Hayward School
(an Essex Education Authority school)
Autism Resource Base
Maltese Road
Chelmsford
Essex CM1 2PA
Tel: 01245 258667

The Helen Allison School
(an NAS school)
Longfield Road
Meopham
Kent
DA13 0EW
Tel: 01474 814878

Hope Lodge School
(a Hampshire Autistic Society school)
22 Midanbury Lane
Bitterne Park
Southampton SO18 4HP
Tel: 01703 634346

Inscape House School
(a Boys and Girls Welfare Society
school)
Schools Hill
Cheadle
Cheshire SK8 1JE
Tel: 0161 283 4750

Lidgett Grove School
(a City of York Educational Services
school)
Wheatlands Grove
Acomb
York   YO26 5NH
Tel: 01904 791437

The Loddon School (independent)
Sherfield on Loddon
Hook
Hants RG27 0JD
Tel: 01256 882394

Kisharon Schools
(a Kisharon Autistic Services school)
Kisharon Day School
(Junior)
1011 Finchley Road
London
NW11 7HB
Tel: 0181 455 7483

Kisharon Autistic Services (Senior
Centre 16+)
37 Moss Hall Grove
London N12 8PE
Tel: 0181 343 9174

Peterhouse School
(an Autism Initiatives school)
Preston New Road
Southport PR9 8PA
Tel: 01704 506682

Portfield School
(a Wessex Autistic Society school)
4 Magdalen Lane
Christchurch
Dorset   BH23 1PH
Tel: 01202 486626

Radlett Lodge School
(an NAS school)
Harper Lane
Radlett
Hertfordshire WD7 9HW
Tel: 01923 854922

Rowan Lodge
(a Devon County Education Authority school)
Oaklands Park School Autism Unit
John Nash Drive
Dawlish
Devon EX7 9SF
Tel: 01626 862363

Storm House School
(an NAS school)
134 Barnsley Road
Wath-upon-Dearne
Rotherham
South Yorkshire S63 6DQ
Tel: 01709 874443

Struan House School
(a Scottish Society for Autistic Children school)
27 Claremont,
Alloa
Clackmannanshire FK10 2DF
Tel: 01259 213435

Sutherland House School
(a Nottingham Regional Society for Autistic Children and Adults school)

Early Years Centre
272 Longdale Lane
Ravenshead
Nottingham NG15 9AH
Tel: 01623 490879

Sutherland House
(primary)
Sutherland Road
Nottingham NG3 7AP
Tel: 0115 987 3375

Sutherland House
(secondary)
Westward
68 Cyprus Road
Mapperley Park
Nottingham NG3 5ED
Tel: 0115 969 1823

The Sybil Elgar School
(an NAS school)
Havelock Road
Southall
Middlesex UB2 4NZ
Tel: 0181 813 9168

Thornhill Park School
(a Tyne & Wear Autistic Society school)
21 Thornhill Park
Sunderland
SR2 7LA
Tel: 0191 514 0659

Treehouse
(a Treehouse Trust school)
21 Huson Close
London NW3 3JW
Tel: 0171 681 9982

Wargrave House School
(a Wargrave House Limited school)
449 Wargrave Road
Newton-le-Willows
Merseyside WA12 8RS
Tel: 01925 224899

Ysgol Plas Brondyffryn
(a Denbighshire County Council school)
Ystrad Road
Denbigh LL16 4RH
Tel: 01745 813841

Adult Centres (in alphabetic order)

Adult Development Service
(a Hampshire Autistic Society service)
Anglesey Lodge
Anglesey Road
Gosport
Hampshire PO12 2DX
Tel: 01705 524243

Agnes House/Albert House
(Alphonsus Homes)
2 Sylvan Green
Hucklow Hill
Halesowen
West Midlands B62 8ER
Tel: 0121 422 5720

Alderson Road
(Northern Life Care)
12 Alderson Road
Harrogate
North Yorkshire HG2 8AS
Tel: 01423 520251

Alfredston Place
(a United Response UK service)
63A Alfredston Place
Wantage
Oxon OX12 8DL
Tel: 01235 772551

Ardcora
(A Downe Residential Project service)
Ardglass Road
Downpatrick
Co Down
Northern Ireland BT30 6RA
Tel: 01396 617110

Ashlar House
(a Leeds Christian Home for Adults
with Autism service)
76 Potternewton Lane
Leeds
West Yorkshire LS7 3LW
Tel: 0113 226 2700

Ashleigh College
(a European Services for People with
Autism service)
3 Elmfield Park
Gosforth
Newcastle-upon-Tyne NE3 4UX
Tel: 0191 213 0833

Avalon House
(Advances in Autism, Care and
Education)
3 King St
Cheltenham
Gloucestershire GL50 4AU
Tel: 01242 695383

Balmyre House
(a Scottish Society for Autistic
Children service)
15 Claremont
Alloa
Clackmannanshire FK10 2DF
Tel: 01259 218433

Bangeston Hall
(Pembrokeshire Resource Centre)
London Road
Pembroke Dock
Pembrokeshire SA72 4RX
Tel: 01646 683173

Binnegar Hall/Purbeck Court
(Krystal Health Care)
East Stoke
Wareham
Dorset BH20 6AT
Tel: 01929 552201

Burnham Service
(an NAS service)
28 Berrow Road
Burnham on Sea
Somerset TA8 2EX
Tel: 01278 792962

Burnside
(North Yorks County Council Social
Services)
1 Burnside
Eastfield
Scarborough YO11 3LH
Tel: 01723 583802

Burton Cottages
(a Sussex Autistic Society service)
Bishops Lane
Robertsbridge
East Sussex TN32 5BA
Tel: 01580 881715

Chippings
(Gresham Care)
28 Russells Crescent
Horley
Surrey RH6 7DN
Tel: 01293 775350

Clannalba House
(a Scottish Society for Autistic
Children service)
Clannalba House
Lamington
Near Biggar ML12 6HP
Tel: 01259 720044

Cloverdale House
(Covertaste Limited)
Abbotsford Grove
Thornholme Road
Thornhill
Sunderland SR7 2JS
Tel: 0191 565 7070

Conchiglia
(A Kingswood Trust service)
Conchiglia
Thrupp Lane
Radley
Nr Abingdon
Oxon OX14 3NG
Tel: 01235 550978

Croydon Service
(an NAS service)
6 St Edwards Close
New Addington
Croydon
Surrey CR0 0EL
Tel: 01689 800960

Day Options Development
(a Brent Social Services service)
Stonebridge Day Centre
Twybridge Way
Hillside
London NW10 0SL
Tel: 0181 961 4489

Dyson's Wood House
(a Disabilities Trust service)
Dyson's Wood
Tokers Green
Reading
Berkshire RG4 9EY
Tel: 0118 972 4553

Fife Unit
(a Scottish Society for Autistic
Children service)
Unit 34
Thistle Industrial Estate
Church St
Cowdenbeath
Fife KY4 8LP
Tel: 01383 610754

Fosse Autism Unit
(Fosse Health Trust service)
Leicester Frith Hospital
Groby Road
Leicester LE3 9QF
Tel: 0116 287 2231

Frank House
(a Hill Park Housing Association Ltd
service)
8a Twigg Close
Erith, Kent DA8 3RD
Tel: 01322 334318

Gammaton Cross
(Satinclose Care Ltd)
East of the Water
Bideford
North Devon EX39 4QE
Tel: 01363 773291

Gloucester Group Homes
(a Gloucestershire Group Homes Trust
service)
Spring Mill Business Centre
Avening Road
Nailsworth
Gloucestershire GL6 0BU
Tel: 01453 835023

Glyncoed
(Maesteilo Care Home)
Cwrt Henn
Dryslwyn
Carmarthenshire
Tel: 01558 668510

Gorse Farm
(a West Midlands Autistic Society
service)
Coleshill Road
Marston Green
Birmingham B37 7HP
Tel: 0121 770 9085

Gravesend Service
(an NAS service)
Overcliffe House
SAND
22-24 Princes St
Gravesend
Kent DA11 0DN
Tel: 01474 535057

Hamilton House
(a Bromley Autistic Trust service)
10 Crescent Road
Bromley BR1 3PW
Tel: 01689 857886

The Hayes Unit
(an NAS service)
Rookery Lane
Pilning
Bristol BS35 4JN
Tel: 01454 632311

Healthlinc House
(Healthlinc House Service)
Cliff Road
Welton
Lincoln
Tel: 01673 862000

Heath Farm
(Lincolnshire Care Services)
Heath Road
Ashby de la Laund
Scopwick, Sleaford
Lincolnshire LN4 3JD
Tel: 01526 320312

High Croft
(a Wessex Autistic Society service)
Whetley Road
Broadwindsor
Beaminster
Dorset DT8 3QT
Tel: 01308 868360

Hucklow Road
(a Mencap service)
19-21 Hucklow Road
Firth Park
Sheffield S5 6TB
Tel: 0114 261 0918

Hyndburn Service
(an NAS service)
Clayton Brook House
90 Atlas St
Clayton-le-Moors
Accrington
Lancashire BB5 5LT
Tel: 01254 301909

InterACT Centre
(The InterACT Centre)
Hanwell Community Centre
Westcott Crescent
Hanwell
London W7 1PD
Tel: 0181 575 0046

Kelsey Care
(Kelsey Care)
1 Old Bexley Lane
Bexley
Kent DA5 5DY
Tel: 01322 621400

Kent Autistic Trust
(a Kent Autistic Trust service)
14 High St
Brompton
Gillingham
Kent ME7 5AE
Tel: 01634 405168

Lambert House
(a Norfolk Autistic Community
Housing Association Ltd)
36 Notridge Road
Bowthorpe
Norwich
Norfolk NR5 9BE
Tel: 01603 749845

Leicester Service
(an NAS service)
19 Camden Road
Braunstone
Leicester LE3 5GF
Tel: 0116 263 0991

The Lodge
(R J Homes)
18 Huntspill Road
Highbridge
Somerset
Tel: 01278 782943

Manchester Service
(an NAS service)
1,3 & 5 Mainwaring Terrace
Northern Moor
Manchester M23 9EW
Tel: 0161 945 0040

18 Marriott Road
(Hoffman de Visme Foundation)
Barnet
London EN5 4NJ
Tel: 0181 449 9493

13 Meadow Avenue
(Horizon NHS Trust)
13 Meadow Avenue
Harperbury Hospital
Harper Lane
Radlett
Herts WD7 9HQ
Tel: 01923 854861 ext 4286/4244

5 Meadow Close
(Horizon NHS Trust)
Harperbury Hospital
Harper Lane
Radlett
Herts WD7 9HQ
Tel: 01923 854861 ext 4275

6 Meadow Close
(Horizon NHS Trust)
Harperbury Hospital
Harper Lane
Radlett
Herts WD7 9HQ
Tel: 01923 854861

Mid/East Lothian Adult Services
(a Scottish Society for Autistic
Children service)
21b North High St
Musselburgh
East Lothian EH21 6JA
Tel: 0131 665 6659

Mildenhall Service
(an NAS service)
Middlefield Manor
The Street
Barton Mills
Bury St Edmunds
Suffolk IP28 6AW
Tel: 01638 716910

Mounthamilton House
(a North Eastern Health Board service)
Carrick Road
Dundalk
Co Louth
Republic of Ireland
Tel: 00353 423 6217

Neath Service
(an NAS service)
Longford Court
Longford
Neath
West Glamorgan SA10 7HN
Tel: 01792 814611

Nevill Park
(Angevin Limited)
4 Nevill Park
Tunbridge Wells, Kent
TN4 8NW
Tel: 01892 519520

Newport Service
(an NAS service)
Orchard House
11a Norman St
Caerleon
Newport
South Wales NP6 1BB
Tel: 01633 423537

Norbury Crescent
(Norcrest Homes Ltd)
30 Norbury Crescent
Norbury
London SW16 4LA
Tel: 0181 765 0431

Norfolk Lodge
(Sussex Health Care)
9 Norfolk Road
Horsham
West Sussex RH12 1BZ
Tel: 01403 218876

Northamptonshire Service
(an NAS service)
Gillitts Road
Wellingborough
Northamptonshire NN8 2HX
Tel: 01933 275525

Oak House
(Community Health Services NHS
Trust Southern Derbyshire)
Aston Hall
Aston on Trent
Derby DE72 2AL
Tel: 01332 792412 Ext 214

Oakfield House
(a West Midlands Autistic Society
service)
6-12 Oakfield Road
Selly Park
Birmingham B29 7EJ
Tel: 0121 471 1913

The Old Rectory
(Satinclose Care Ltd)
27 Stallard St
Trowbridge
Wiltshire BA14 9AA
Tel: 01225 777728

Peldon Old Rectory
(an Essex Autistic Society service)
Church Road
Peldon
Nr Colchester
Essex CO5 7PT

Pelicans FE College
(Pelicans FE College Service)
St Mary's Road
Meare
Glastonbury
Somerset BA6 9SP
Tel: 01458 860536

**Queen Elizabeth The Queen
Mother Centre**
(a Hertfordshire Autistic Community
Trust service)
Station Road
Bricket Wood
St Albans
Hertfordshire AL2 3PJ
Tel: 01923 678523

Raby Hall
(a Wirral Autistic Society service)
Raby Hall Road
Bromborough
Wirral L63 0NN
Tel: 0151 334 7510

Ravenswood
(a Nottingham Regional Society for
Autistic Children and Adults service)
34 Ilkeston Road
Heanor
Derbyshire DE75 7DT
Tel: 01773 769278

Ridgepark House
(a Scottish Society for Autistic
Children service)
Mousebank Road
Lanark ML11 7RA
Tel: 01555 665988

Robleaze House
(Mrs S Robinson)
537-539 Bath Road
Brislington
Bristol BS4 3LB
Tel: 0117 972 0813

Rogerstone House
(Community Care Associates)
73 Risca Road
Rogerstone
Newport
Gwent
Tel: 01633 614365

St Erme House
(a Devon and Cornwall Autistic
Community Trust service)
St Erme
Nr Truro
Cornwall TR4 9BW
Tel: 01872 279198

St Marks
(Mr & Mrs Dominic Kennard)
23 Collier Road
West Hill
Hastings TN34 3JR
Tel: 01424 200854

Seaham Community
(a European Services for People with
Autism service)
The Old Vicarage
Station Road
Seaham
Co Durham SR7 9BG
Tel: 0191 213 0833

11 Serlby Close
(a Northgate & Prudhoe NHS Trust
service)
Coach Road
High Usworth
Washington
Tyne & Wear NE37 1EN
Tel: 0191 415 5041

Somerset Court
(an NAS service)
Harp Road
Brent Knoll
Somerset TA9 4HQ
Tel: 01278 760555

South Hill College
(a European Services for People with
Autism service)
9 The Cedars
Ashbrooke
Sunderland SR2 7TW
Tel: 0191 567 3523

South Lodge Group Home
(Surrey Oaklands NHS Trust)
St Ebba's Hospital
Hook Road
Epsom KT19 8QJ
Tel: 01372 202020

Spring Lake
(Waterhouse Ltd)
17 Forty Lane
Wembley Park
Middlesex HA9 9EU
Tel: 0181 908 5233

The Springs Community
(The Springs Community Ltd)
Coast Drive
St Mary's Bay
Kent TN29 9HN
Tel: 01797 363550

Starbeck
(North Yorks County Council Social
Services)
80 High Street
Starbeck
Harrogate HG2 7LW
Tel: 01423 883301

Stroud Court
(a Stroud Court Community Trust
service)
Longfords
Minchinhampton
Gloucestershire GL6 9AN
Tel: 01453 834020

Surrey Service
(an NAS service)
42-44 Stonepit Close
Godalming
Surrey GU7 2LS
Tel: 01483 861066

Thehela House
(Hallow Residential Home Care
Limited)
144 Hagden Lane
Watford
WD1 8NH
Tel: 01707 873877

Thornbeck College
(a Tyne & Wear Autistic Society
service)
14 Thornhill Park
Sunderland SR2 7LA
Tel: 0191 510 2038

Thorne House
(Thorne House Services for
Autism)
St Nicholas Road
Thorne
Doncaster
South Yorkshire DN8 5BG
Tel: 01405 812128

Tower House
(South Devon Autism Resource
Centre Ltd)
Tower House
34 Higher Brimley Road
Teignmouth
Devon TQ14 8JU
Tel: 01626 776515

West London Service
(an NAS service)
Unit 12
Cranleigh Gardens Industrial Estate
Cranleigh Gardens
Southall
Middlesex UB1 2BZ
Tel: 0181 571 7714

Whitegates
(a Nottingham Regional Society for
Autistic Children and Adults
service)
Sparken Hill
Worksop
Nottinghamshire S80 1AP
Tel: 01909 478746

Whitstone
(a Norfolk Autistic Community
Housing Association Ltd service)
49 Norwich Road
Dereham
Norfolk NR20 3AS
Tel: 01362 698762

Wood Dene
(Stepping Stones Homes
(Wakefield) Ltd)
Colliery Approach
Outwood
Wakefield WF3 3JH
Tel: 01924 825252

Woodend
(The Lothlorien Community
Limited)
Cannongate
Hythe
Kent CT21 5PX
Tel: 01303 230131

Woodside Villa
(Northgate & Prudhoe NHS Trust)
Northgate Hospital
Morpeth
Northumberland NE61 3BP
Tel: 01670 394000

Wycar Leys House
(Wycar Leys House)
Kirklington Road
Old Bilsthorpe
Nottingham NG22 8TT
Tel: 01623 871752

Yad Voezer Hostel
(Yad Voezer Service)
80 Queen Elizabeth's Walk
London N16 5UP
Tel: 0181 809 4303

Chapter 25

Branches and affiliated local autistic societies

NAS Branches

NAS Branches organise various activities for the whole family. Branches provide mutual support by way of talks and sharing of information, social activities and awareness-raising among professionals and the general public. For details of your nearest Branch contact your local Development Officer:

South West and Mid-Counties
Jan Snook, Development Manager
Tel: 0117 987 2575

South East
Tracey Sellers, Development Officer
Tel: 0171 903 3557

London and East Anglia
Greg Pasco, Development Officer
Tel: 0171 903 3557

East Midlands and North East
Alan Bicknell, Development Officer
Tel: 0115 911 3360

North West and West Midlands
Chris Barson, Development Officer
Tel: 0115 911 3360

Wales
Delyth Elward, Development Officer
Tel: 01792 815915

Scotland
Gill West, Development Manager
Tel: 0141 221 8090

Affiliated local autistic societies

All Lewisham Autism Support
117 Manor Avenue
Brockley
London SE4 1PE

Asperger Syndrome Association of Ireland
New Road
Greystones
County Wicklow

Autism Bedfordshire
St Mark's Church Community Centre
Calder Rise/Avon Drive
Bedfordshire MK41 7UY

Autistic Society for the Greater Manchester Area
25 Mulgrave Street
Swinton
Greater Manchester M27 9XH

Berkshire Autistic Society
103 London Road
Reading
Berks RG1 5BY

Bromley Autistic Trust
366B Crofton Road
Locksbottom
Orpington
Kent BR6 8NN

Cambridgeshire Autistic Society
1 Potton Road
Hilton
Huntingdon
Cambridge PE18 9NG

Children in Touch
45 Lower Road
Chinnor
Oxfordshire OX9 4DU

Derbyshire Autistic Support Group
The Cottage
Crich Chase Farm
Chase Road, Ambergate
Derbyshire DE56 2HA

Devon and Cornwall Autistic Community Trust
Trafalgar House
Malpas Road
Truro
TR1 1QH

Devon and Cornwall Autistic Society
The Cottage
1 Old Pond Lane
Redruth
Cornwall
TR15 1DN

East Anglian Autistic Support Trust
52 Windsor Road
Cambridge
CB4 3JN

Edinburgh Autistic Playschemes
18/6 Northfield Drive
Edinburgh
EH8 7RP

Essex Autistic Society
12 St Peters Court
St Peters Street
Colchester
Essex, CO1 1WJ

European Services for People with Autism
South Hill College
9 The Cedars
Ashbrooke
Sunderland SR2 7TW

Gloucestershire Group Homes
Irving Cottage
89 Main Road
Naphill
High Wycombe
Bucks, HP14 4RT

Gwent Autistic Society
105 Allt-Yr-Yn Avenue
Newport
Gwent
South Wales
NP9 5 DE

Hampshire Autistic Society
1634 Parkway
Solent Business Park
Whitely
Fareham
Hampshire PO15 7AH

Help for Able Autistic Adults
42 Parkhill Road
Bexley
Kent DA5 1HU

Hertfordshire Autistic Community Trust
Queen Mother Resource Centre
Station Road
Bricket Wood
St Albans AL2 3PJ

Highlands Autistic Playschemes Initiative
17 Shiel Square
Achareidh
Nairn
IV12 4SS

Hill Park Housing Association Ltd
11a Pembury Road
Bexleyheath
Kent
DA7 5LW

Hillingdon Autistic Care and Support (HACS)
22 Cherry Grove
Hillingdon UB8 3ET

Hyndburn & East Lancashire Autistic Society
21 Cedar Street
Accrington
Lancashire BB5 6SQ

Isle of Man Support Group
5 Killeaba Mount
Ramsey
Isle of Man IM8 2JG

Isle of Wight Autistic Society
28 Place Side
Cowes
Isle of Wight PO31 7BB

Kent Autistic Trust
14 High Street
Brompton
Gillingham
Kent, ME7 5AE

Leeds and District Autism, Behaviour, Communication Support Group
72 Holtdale Way
Holt Park
Leeds LS16 7SJ

Leeds Christian Homes for Adults with Autism
76 Potternewton Lane
Leeds
West Yorkshire LS7 3LW

Leicestershire Autistic Society
314 Hinckley Road
Leicester
Leicestershire
LE3 0TN

Lincolnshire Autistic Society
21 Mill Lane
Donington
Spalding
Lincolnshire PE11 4TL

Norfolk Autistic Community Housing Association
Whitstone, 49 Norwich Road
Dereham
Norfolk NR20 3AS

Norfolk Autistic Society
Charing Cross Centre
17-19 St John Maddermarket
Norwich
Norfolk NR2 1DN

North Eastern Autistic Society
645 Marton Road
Middlesborough
Cleveland
TS4 3SE

North Wales Autistic Society
1 Waun Road
Glanwyffwn
Gwynedd
LL31 9JW

Northamptonshire Society for Autism
Suite 35
Burlington House
369 Wellingborough Road
Northampton, NN1 4ET

NoRSACA
348a Carlton Hill
Nottingham NG4 1JB

Oxfordshire Autistic Society for Information and Support (OASIS)
7 Mileway Gardens
Headington
Oxfordshire OX3 7XH

**Parents and Professionals and
Autism (PAPA)**
Graham House
Knockbracken Healthcare
Saintfield Road
Belfast BT8 8BH

Perth Action on Autism
4 Tarrylaw Farm
Balbeggie
Tayside
PH2 6HL

**Renfrewshire Autism and Asperger
Group**
Garthdee
1 Millbrae,
Bridge of Weir
Renfrewshire PA11 3LB

Sheffield Autistic Society
24 Alms Road
Ecclesall
Sheffield
South Yorkshire S11 4NX

Strathclyde Autistic Society
549 Crow Road
Glasgow G13 1NY

**South & Mid Glamorgan Autistic
Society**
52 Woodlands Avenue
Mid Glamorgan CF35 6UP

South Wales Autistic Society
2 Mallard Way
Porthcawl
Mid Glamorgan CF36 3TS

Stroud Court Community Trust
Stroud Court
Longfords
Minchinhampton
Gloucester GL6 9AN

Surrey Autistic Community Trust
22 The Ridgeway
Leatherhead
Surrey KT22 9AZ

Sussex Autistic Society
PO Box 2540
Rottingdean
Brighton BN2 8ST

**Thorne House Services for Autism
Ltd**
Thorne House St Nicholas Road
Thorne
Nr Doncaster
South Yorkshire DN8 5BG

Tyne & Wear Autistic Society
22 Coleridge Drive
Sherborne Park, Stokeford
Choppington
Northumberland NE62 5HD

Wargrave House Ltd
449 Wargrave Road
Newton-Le-Willows
Merseyside WA12 8RS

Wessex Autistic Society
39 Bargates
Christchurch
Dorset BH23 1QD

West Midlands Autistic Society
17B Fellows Lane
Harborne
Birmingham
West Midlands B17 9TS

Wirral Autistic Society
Raby Hall
Raby Hall Road
Bromborough
Wirral, Merseyside L63 0NN

Index to Advertisers

Index